Physicist and Christian

WILLIAM G. POLLARD

Physicist and Christian

A DIALOGUE
BETWEEN THE COMMUNITIES

THE SEABURY PRESS · NEW YORK

First *Seabury Paperback* edition published 1964

Library of Congress Catalog Card Number: 61-14381
364-869-C-9-3.5
Printed in the United States of America

Third Printing

PHYSICIST AND CHRISTIAN: *originally given as The Bishop Paddock Lectures (1959) at The General Theological Seminary, New York City.*

ACKNOWLEDGMENTS

Grateful acknowledgment is made to the following publishers and authors for permission to quote from the copyrighted titles listed:

The Christian Scholar—Harold K. Schilling, "On Relating Science and Religion" (41:376)
Harper's Magazine—Werner Heisenberg, "A Scientist's Case for the Classics" (May 1958)
Oxford University Press—Rudolph Otto, *The Idea of the Holy*, tr. by John W. Harvey
Pantheon Books, Inc.—Werner Heisenberg, *Philosophical Problems of Nuclear Science*
Michael Polanyi and the University of Chicago Press—Michael Polanyi, *Personal Knowledge*
Science—Harold K. Schilling, "A Human Enterprise" (127:1324)
Charles Scribner's Sons—Martin Buber, *I and Thou*
Simon and Schuster, Inc.—J. Robert Oppenheimer, *Science and the Common Understanding* (copyright 1954)
Student Christian Movement Press, Ltd.—Karl Heim, *Christian Faith and Natural Science;* J. H. Oldham, *Life Is Commitment*
University of Chicago Press—Robert Redfield, *The Little Community* (copyright 1955 by the University of Chicago)
University of Toronto Press—Harcourt Brown, ed., *Science and the Creative Spirit*
Viking Press—Arthur Miller, *The Crucible*
Yale University Press—Edmund Fuller, ed., *The Christian Idea of Education*

Dedicated

to the Memory of my Son

JAMIE

Preface

THE ROLE of community as a central aspect of Christian life and experience within the Body of Christ has lately been receiving prominent attention, particularly in the Episcopal Church. The program of Parish Life Conferences, Church and Group Life Laboratories, and other activities applying the insights of secular Group Dynamics to the Church has been a major emphasis of the American branch of the Anglican Communion throughout the last decade. This emphasis has found a sympathetic response in my own experience of coming into the Church during this same period. In reflecting on this experience, I have come to see the community as the primary source of the new insights and understandings which have come to me as a result of incorporation in it.

It is, however, a somewhat different aspect of community than that commonly emphasized which has come to concern me in a primary way. This is the connection between community and knowledge. What I have come to realize is that the transition accomplished in me over the past decade from a merely formal adherence to the outward forms of Christianity to the confidence and conviction in the truth and validity of the Apostolic Faith which I now enjoy was really accomplished by the power of the Christian community to reveal or unfold such knowledge to those incorporated in it. This thought raised in turn the broader question of whether it might not be the case that all knowledge is really imparted through community, and cannot be had in isolation or alienation from the community within which a particular segment of knowledge is known.

In parallel with this line of thought I was experiencing at the same time an increasing uneasiness and discontent with the contrast between the reception which the world at large accorded me as a physicist and as a Christian priest. The mid-twentieth century is an age which axiomatically grants truth and validity to scientific knowledge, but equally axiomatically discounts religious knowledge as mere opinion. This presents no problem to one conformed to the pervading convictions of his age. But to me, for whom the new range of reality I had come to know as a Christian was just as valid and substantial as the range of reality I knew as a physicist, it was a problem which acquired a primary importance in my thinking. I found myself increasingly concerned to try to understand the underlying reasons for this dichotomy between my own convictions and those of the world about me.

Several years ago I had the privilege of collaborating with Harold K. Schilling in the conduct of a Danforth Foundation Seminar for college science teachers at the Pennsylvania State University. Out of this association has grown a close friendship and a very helpful continuing discourse in the general area of the knowledge of reality in science and in Christianity. One of Dean Schilling's lectures in particular during this seminar struck me with great force and has subsequently proven to be an illuminating and fruitful path of inquiry which has stood up well during the intervening years. This lecture dealt with much the same ideas and approach as that of the first chapter in this book. The effect of it was to let me realize for the first time that the same emphasis on community which was quite natural and generally understood in the acquisition of Christian knowledge within the Church could be applied in a remarkably parallel fashion to my earlier experience of coming to know physics through my personal involvement in and commitment to the community of physicists.

The invitation to deliver the Bishop Paddock Lectures at the General Theological Seminary in 1959 provided the opportunity to attempt an orderly and systematic development of these ideas. This book contains these lectures substantially as they were given except that each chapter contains about twice as much material as that actually used in the corresponding lecture. The first half of the book is devoted to the nature and function of community as I have known it in both physics and Christianity. The last half is concerned with the role of community in empowering those within it to acquire knowledge of that portion of reality external to themselves which the particular community possesses. It is this mutual interdependence of the two themes of community and knowledge which constitutes the unity of the book and ties together its two halves.

After my first introduction to Dean Schilling's ideas on science as community, I developed my own thoughts along these lines in a lecture which I subsequently gave on a number of university campuses. These trials resulted in several modifications of the lecture based on audience reaction and discussion with university people. At a late stage of this development, this lecture was given as one of the addresses of the Academic Symposia which were a part of the Centennial of Iowa State College in 1958. In this form it was published in the volume of Commemorative Papers from the Centennial. The permission of the Iowa State College Press for the reuse of this material in an expanded form as the first chapter of this book is gratefully acknowledged.

A portion of Chapter IV also was originally given as one of the Raymond Collyer Knox Memorial Lectures at Columbia University in 1954 as a part of the celebration of Columbia's Bicentennial Year. This lecture was published in *The Christian*

Scholar (March, 1955) under the title, "An Inquiry into the Status of Non-Conceptual Experience." The permission of the publishers of this journal for the reuse of this material in this volume is also gratefully acknowledged. The earlier form has, however, been substantially rewritten for the present purpose, and the concluding section of the chapter is new.

Any clergyman who has had the privilege of attending one of the conferences at the College of Preachers at the Washington Cathedral will recognize when they read Chapter III my direct debt to the former Warden, the Reverend Canon Theodore O. Wedel, particularly in the extensive use I have made of his analogy between the Holy Spirit in the Church and the spirit of a human organization such as the Marine Corps. My debt to Canon Wedel and to the College of Preachers goes much deeper, however, than this direct borrowing of what to me was a very revealing idea. Indeed it was the experience of my first conference there in 1952, just before my ordination to the Diaconate, that helped me understand the full power of the Christian community to open the eyes of those incorporated in it so as to behold and to know the living God who is revealed in Christ. Those who have shared the communal life of the College, the Holy Eucharists in the mornings, the sung Compline in the evenings, Canon Wedel's meditations on Romans or Ephesians, and his lectures on various aspects of the Faith, will know just what I mean by this. Many of the insights and understandings throughout this book are ultimately derived from my repeated exposure to this great institution and to those who make the Faith live within it.

When I reflect on the profound effect on me of my experience in depth of the Christian community at the College of Preachers, I am struck by the parallel to this of an earlier experience of community which also took place in the City of Washington. This occurred in the mid-thirties when as a young physicist I first started attending the spring meetings of the American Physical Society which were then held at the Bureau of Standards. There all the great figures of American physics would gather each year and share with each other the excitement and the passion of the quest for understanding in which we were all engaged. For a young man just joining in this quest, these meetings, and especially the small informal groups sitting on the lawn around the building where the formal presentation of papers was going on, were an unforgettable experience. It was here in the very heart of the community of physics that one would really come to know physics. And so, for me, these two places in Washington, the Bureau of Standards and the College of Preachers, have come to symbolize that fundamental relationship between knowledge and community, as I have experienced it in both physics and Christianity, which it is the purpose of this book to explore and to clarify.

W. G. P.

Oak Ridge, Tennessee
April, 1961

Contents

I

Community vs. Subject Matter

WHEN science and religion are compared, it is usually in terms of subject matter, methods of acquiring knowledge, or the truth about reality which each represents. There is, however, another, and quite different, way in which they can be discussed. This arises from the fact that each is in essence a community within which a certain characteristic kind of life is led. In my own case I have come to share fully in the life of two communities. First I was drawn into the community of physics and came to know and to share in its life as a physicist among other physicists. Later I was drawn into the community of the faithful in Christ Jesus, which is the Church, and have come to know and to share in its life as a Christian among other Christians. The sharing in the life of these two communities has profoundly affected me as a person. Each has contributed in a major way to the process of self-discovery and self-formation. They have had a large role in making me what I am today.

It is easy when speaking of physics or any other science to ignore even the existence of the community. What comes to mind instead is a subject with a certain content dealing with matter and energy, space and time, force and motion, and the like. Along with this subject matter one would also be likely to think of the instruments and apparatus which make up physics and are an integral part of it, such things as calorimeters, spectroscopes, galvanometers, Geiger counters, and cyclotrons. All this and much more besides is indeed physics. At the same time, however, we must never forget that all of it, subject matter and instruments alike, is the product and the achievement of a human communal enterprise. For several centuries there has been in continuous historic existence a community of men who have shared a common passion for an activity which has produced all that comes to mind when we think of physics. In each new generation this community has drawn into itself new members and incorporated them into its life. It is this community which has devised and constructed all the instruments and techniques which make up physics. The subject matter that physics possesses today is the result of the corporate imagination and labor of human persons in community. This, of course, is an obvious statement once it has been made. Yet it is remarkable how rarely it is recognized as a relevant, not to say essential, element of any science.

My ordination to the diaconate several years ago brought with it a mounting pressure for me to speak and write on subjects related to the general topic of science and religion. By now I have done a considerable amount of both lecturing and writing on various aspects of this general topic. But as little as a decade ago I had not written or said anything on the subject, with the exception of a few papers done for undergraduate courses which were simply antagonistic to the idea of religion. It has been illuminating to me to reflect on the transformation which took place in those intervening ten years with the object of trying to identify the source of the capacity acquired during them for engaging in theological thought. The question arises, how is it that a person with no background or understanding in theology is turned into one who can deal in an informed and meaningful way with live theological questions?

In seeking an answer to this question, it occurred to me that precisely the same question could be raised with respect to the much earlier process which brought me into physics. In that instance, too, there was a ten-year period from about age 15 to age 25, during which the transformation from non-physicist to physicist took place. A person who, to begin with, had no acquaintance with physics and was not in any way identified with it by his contemporaries was converted, in a relatively brief span, into one who confidently took on, and grappled with, tough problems on the frontier of physics in a way which met with the acceptance and approval of those who had long been established as physicists. In looking back on this experience with the object of seeking some insight into this change, I have become more and more aware of the remarkable parallel existing between the two transformations in my life. From the biographical standpoint alone, the process by which a person becomes a Christian, it appears, has many close similarities to that by which he becomes a physicist. It will be the burden of much that follows to show that the most revealing insights on these transformations are derived by seeing each as a process of incorporation into a community.

There is a widespread impression that advance in knowledge of subject matter is the basis for such transformations as we have been discussing. More specifically, it is generally supposed that one first learns all about physics or Christianity, their factual matter, content, methods, and ways of knowing, and then on the basis of such knowledge decides whether he wishes to become a physicist or a Christian. In my experience this widespread popular impression is completely erroneous. I am convinced that real knowledge and understanding in either case comes well after, not before, such a decision has been made. I do not really know or understand the process by which as a young man I became interested in physics and soon decided that I wanted to be a physicist. Whatever that process was, it was not based on a knowledge of physics. On the contrary, I am convinced that until I had already made the decision to become a physicist, I could not even begin to really learn physics. In the same way the process which led me into full involvement in the Church is equally mysterious to me. It certainly was not the result of an exhaustive study of Christianity. Rather it is clear to me in retrospect that only after I had made my decision and my incorporation into the Church was nearly complete, did I have a secure enough platform on which to stand in order to grapple meaningfully or fruitfully with tough theological questions. This, however, is just another way of expressing the central theological affirmation that it is by grace, not works, that one becomes a Christian. To this affirmation I would add that it was also, in a completely analogous way, by grace, not by knowledge, that I became a physicist.

Subject Matter Does Not Stand Alone

Both physics and Christianity have acquired an extensive subject matter. In each case the subject matter is important, even central. Were its subject matter removed, either one would become empty and pointless. Yet each is much more than its subject matter, and it is this overplus beyond mere intellectual content which I am concerned to elucidate. For, in each case, the community is in an important sense prior to the subject matter content. Thus the content of Christianity in its entirety has all been produced, preserved, and transmitted by the community, the Church. Apart from the Church there would have been no subject matter. In the same way the content of physics in its entirety has all been acquired, preserved, and transmitted by the community of physicists. Apart from this community there would not have been any such thing as physics.

One way to see the force of this point for any one of the sciences is to consider the problems which arise when an attempt is made to formulate an adequate and satisfactory definition of the specific science in terms of subject matter. At the beginning of an introductory course to the science this must somehow be attempted, for the students who have registered for the course expect to be told at the outset what the subject is about. The instructor, however, in trying to formulate some adequate statement for meeting this natural, and apparently quite proper, need generally finds himself in difficulty. How, for example, can a boundary be staked out in the natural world which will clearly and adequately distinguish physics from chemistry? The deeper one goes into this task, the more difficult and complex it is seen to be. Every definition of either subject which recommends itself is soon seen to have numerous loopholes. The fields overlap each other, and the boundaries continually shift with new progress in each science. Many who have faced up to this problem have in the end suggested in desperation that the best definition of physics is that it consists of everything done by physicists. From the standpoint of physics as subject matter this definition is facetious, but from the standpoint of physics as community it is profound.

In actual practice little effort or interest is expended on such definitions. In time, as the course goes on, the students will come to acquire a feel for what physics is. In part this comes from the content of the textbook and lectures, the experiments and examinations, which, as the course unfolds, gradually reveal the nature of the subject. But this is only in part. Even more important is the character and structure of the life which goes on inside the physics building or the chemistry building. Each is distinctive and recognizable. Although it may be difficult to tell the difference between physics and chemistry as subjects, there is no trouble at all when it comes to telling the difference between a physicist and a chemist. They are clearly members of two different, distinct, and contrasting communities. The student, along with the rest of the university, comes to think of physics as that which goes on in the physics building, whereas chemistry takes place in the chemistry building.

Another way to see science as community is to consider the history of each science. When we do this what immediately stands out is the unity and coherence of the men and women who have been engaged in it. Physics, for example, has changed radically in subject matter over the years. First it was interested in the laws of motion of bodies; later with the properties of substances, heat, energy, and light. Then in the last half of the last century electricity and magnetism were the dominant interest. With the discovery of the electron the center of interest turned to atoms and molecules, and more recently to atomic nuclei. Now the growing family of strange unstable particles produced at ultra-high energies is the center of interest. None of the early physicists could possibly have foreseen the course of this path of inquiry. Yet physicists today can still read the papers of Newton, Joule, Hamilton, Faraday, and Lorenz and feel at home with them. Whatever the subject under investigation, the peculiar combination of attitudes, values, standards, and expectations which uniquely pervades the community of physics is recognizably present. Quite clearly these are kindred spirits and fellow physicists, even though the content of physics has become for us something vastly different than it was for them. They approach a problem in the same way, apply the same critical standards to their treatment of it, and share the same criteria of excellence for its solution.

Ancient Greece produced a few isolated instances of genius, such as Democritus and Archimedes, who investigated physical problems. But it did not produce physics. Only when such isolated individual sparks caught fire and spread so as to draw men into a communal enterprise did what we know now as physics emerge. When this happened, a community came into being possessed of a unique power of inquiry into nature. Its members were seized with this power and shared in the dynamic vitality and enthusiasm of it. The spirit of this community has been the same ever since in spite of the way in which the objects of its inquiries have continuously changed and spread. It has throughout commanded from its members a common loyalty, imposed upon them a common discipline, and conferred upon them common rewards and satisfactions. So, too, it has been with the other sciences which have emerged in the last few centuries. Each owed its birth to the formation of a special community of inquiry peculiar to itself. One man is not enough, no matter what his genius. Only when others catch his fire and his vision and join him to labor in a common quest for understanding does a science come into being.

A Continuing Community Is Essential

The same aspect can be seen in the educational process by which each science reproduces itself and maintains itself from one generation to another. This process is very different in nature and character from what is commonly supposed. Many people look upon science as a sort of vast impersonal mechanism which people can be trained to operate as they would a lathe or a locomotive. It is thought to be a self-correcting procedure which automatically generates infallible information about nature by the application to phenomena of a mechanical process known as "the scientific method." Nothing could be further from the truth about science as it is known from the inside to those who live it and do it. Education in a science is a gradual process of incorporation into a community. The process, to be effective, must expose the student to the spirit of the community so that he becomes infected by it. He must, of course, master a large body of factual material and acquire many specialized instrumental and intellectual skills. But much more than this, he must somehow come to share the characteristic viewpoint and attitude of his science toward phenomena. Through intimate continued contact with his professors, he discovers how they react to the frustrations and ambiguities of research, becomes aware of the sources of their confidence in the ultimate fruitfulness of their enterprise, and learns how to subject himself to the rigorous discipline which the enterprise entails. He must hear, too, about the great personalities in his science, and this must include not only their scientific achievements but also tales and yarns about their foibles, personal peculiarities, and escapades as well. Gradually he comes to share in the sense of adventure, the excitement of discovery, and the hope in triumphs to come which energize the community. Ultimately he reaches the point at which both he and his professors recognize that he has become one of them. He is a physicist, or chemist, or psychologist. Not only does he feel himself to be one, but when he goes to a professional meeting he finds that others instinctively respond to him as such. He has been incorporated into the community.

Those who look on scientific education as a purely mechanical process of imparting information and skills often fail to see the importance of research and argue in favor of dispensing with the thesis requirement. But when we think of graduate education as incorporation into a community, this matter emerges in a different light. For it is only in research that the student can be confronted directly with nature on his own, and, under the watchful guidance of his professors, discover whether he too really can possess the intuitions and ingenuity, the discipline, and the confidence and faith which give the community its power to grapple with nature and emerge with new understandings. It is only in carrying out research on his own that the student can feel, and others can realize, that he has indeed become one of them, a full participant in the life and power of the community.

The extent to which any science is in its essential structure a human community has been cogently summed up in a recent article in *Science* by Harold K. Schilling:

> Without doubt the term *science community,* heard with increasing frequency, is extremely useful in describing science as it actually is. Certainly it does exist—and it is a community with the usual attributes of human communities. It has its own ideals and characteristic way of life; its own standards, mores, conventions, signs and symbols, language and jargon, professional ethics, sanctions and controls, authority, institutions and organizations, publications; its own creeds and beliefs, orthodoxies and heresies—and effective ways of dealing with the latter. This community is affected, as are other communities, by the usual vagaries, adequacies, and shortcomings of human beings. It has its politics, its pulling and hauling, its pressure groups; its differing schools of thought, its divisions and schisms; its personal loyalties and animosities, jealousies, hatreds, and rallying cries; its fads and fashions.

The entire article from which this passage is quoted is of great value in clarifying further the idea which has been developed in the foregoing paragraphs.

It is, of course, the same with Christianity, although the extent to which religion has come to be regarded as a private and individual affair may tend to mask this fact. Any view of Christianity which does not make community its very essence is foreign to the whole spirit of the New Testament. All of the great New Testament images of the Christian life are profoundly communal. Christians are "members of the household of God," "fellow citizens with the saints," living stones built into a holy temple for a dwelling place for God, the Holy Spirit, "a chosen race, a royal priesthood, a holy nation, God's own people," members of the very Body of Christ. No more exalted vision of the strength and power of human community has ever been had than that which emerged from the Church in these first writings which she produced. A conversion to Christianity which does not involve at the same time full incorporation into this community with a consequent full sharing in the common life in the Body of Christ is impoverished and impotent. It would be like trying to become a physicist without sharing in the life and work of the fellowship of physics and in a state of alienation from the community of physicists. This, indeed, is the meaning and basis of the assertion that there is no salvation outside the Catholic Church. The very idea of salvation apart from full incorporation into the holy fellowship is incongruous from the Biblical standpoint. The old covenant was made with a people, Israel, and individuals shared in it only as members of Israel. So too the new covenant is through Christ with a people, his Church, and individuals can share in it only as members of the Church.

Demonstration *vs.* Blind Acceptance

A number of the contrasts which are frequently made between science and religion are seen to be either wrong or irrelevant as soon as the true nature of science as community is recognized. Consider, for example, the common assertion that anyone can demonstrate the truths of science for himself, but the tenets of religion have to be accepted blindly on faith. Anyone who has ever taught a science knows how few people there are who can really demonstrate a scientific truth to their own satisfaction. How many, for example, can demonstrate to their own inner satisfaction that the acceleration due to gravity is 32 feet per second per second? When we go beyond an elementary demonstration such as this and consider the whole range of truth about the nature of physical reality which physics has uncovered, then the number of people with the capacity to demonstrate these truths is severely limited. A long, hard educational process is required during which a person must freely submit himself to a rigorous discipline, and ardently desire and believe in its outcome before he can acquire for himself the power to demonstrate the truths of science to his own satisfaction. Indeed, this process is none other than that which we have just described as the process of incorporation into the community. Only by becoming a physicist can he possess the capacity to demonstrate the truths of physics to his own satisfaction. Only physicists can really know the truth of physics; everyone else has to take it on faith. And this is equally true of Christianity. The Church, too, is a community whose distinctive life and unique power of understanding can only be shared by those who have subjected themselves to the full process of incorporation into that community. Only those who have really done so can know the profound truths to which she bears witness. Only Christians can really know the truth of Christianity; everyone else has to take it, if at all, on faith.

The truth of this simple fact can be seen by considering the problem of popularizing science. There is a radical difference in communication when I as a physicist present a paper to fellow physicists at a meeting of the American Physical Society, and when I give a popular lecture on some aspect of modern physics to a general audience. In conversation or exposition with fellow physicists a minimum of words suffices for a maximum of communication. Nothing can compare with the high level of appreciation which such an audience has to offer for a really good piece of work well done, nor with the incisive and penetrating criticism which it metes out in response to poor work. But with the popular audience, on the other hand, no amount of ingenuity or care can achieve any real sense of having really put across the point. Most particularly it is quite impossible to convey to a general audience the peculiar mixture of tentativeness and confidence which physicists instinctively feel about the knowledge they have gained. This situation is, however, in my experience not confined to science. In exactly the same way I experience the same contrast when I speak concerning the Faith to, on the one hand, a group of fellow clergy or theologians, or, on the other, give a lecture on Christianity to a random academic audience. Such experiences have convinced me that the only way to really know the truth of physics is to become a physicist, and the only way to really know the truth of Christianity is to become a fully-committed Christian.

Public vs. Private Knowledge

This last point suggests another contrast which is frequently made, namely, that science deals with public knowledge while religion is confined to private, subjective knowledge. This again reflects not so much an insight into the proper nature of either, as it does a prejudice peculiar to the twentieth-century cultural context. It is true that when I give a popular lecture as a physicist, I can count on having an audience which is spontaneously and even subconsciously convinced in advance of the validity, importance, and undeniable truth of the enterprise of physics as a whole. Moreover, the idea that I might speak of a private physics of my own would not even occur to them. I have never yet been called upon by a modern audience to defend myself or explain what possessed me to embrace physics. It is equally true that whenever I give a popular lecture on a theological topic, I can count on having an audience equally convinced in advance that religion, although possibly proper, respectable, and even admirable, is nevertheless a private peculiarity of individual people and therefore essentially unreal. Here the idea of a Catholic faith which is the common public witness of the whole body of the faithful through the ages is alien to contemporary ways of thinking about Christianity. I can almost always count on being called upon by puzzled people to explain what possessed me to embrace such a faith with the degree of seriousness implied by my taking Holy Orders.

In this sense it is true that in the twentieth century science is public knowledge and religion is private. But it has often struck me that had God given it to me to live in the sixth century or even the twelfth instead of the twentieth, the situation would have been exactly reversed. Had I spoken on Christianity in that period, my audience would have been spontaneously convinced in advance of the complete validity and universal truth of what I represented, and it would have seemed completely natural that I should want to be a priest of the Church. On the other hand, if I had then subsequently become interested in the works of Democritus and Archimedes and fascinated by Greek physics, it would have seemed an anomalous thing for a well-established cleric to do. I would certainly then have been called upon to explain over and over to puzzled people what could cause a priest to divert himself whole-heartedly and zestfully into an enterprise as private and subjective as physics. Conversely, in any talk on physics then, I could have counted on an audience prepared in advance to hear only a private testimonial to an inner experience, interesting perhaps, but basically unreal and unimportant. In the sixth century Christianity would have represented public knowledge and science would have been called private knowledge.

From my standpoint, in contrast to that of the culture in which I am placed, my relationship to Christianity is no different in its essentials from my relationship to physics. In both cases I was moved to respond to a great public body of truth, existing prior to my response to it and continuing after I shall be gone; a public body of truth external to me and standing over against me as an individual Christian or physicist. I do not any more have a faith of my own than I have a physics of my own. Nor, from my point of view, was the basis on which I sought and was made a priest of the Church any more admirable or praiseworthy than the basis on which I became a physicist. In either case the idea of seeking some private knowledge of my own, an inner fabrication of my own making designed to give me comfort, "peace of mind," or subjective security, could not have supported the degree of commitment and involvement which both physics and Christianity have elicited from me. Yet this viewpoint is alien to the way of thinking about religion in our age, and is extremely difficult to communicate to others. I am convinced that the historic Catholic faith is an image of reality which in essence is just as public and objectively real as is the whole theoretical structure which constitutes modern physics. But the world in which I live largely rejects the former as being artificially dogmatic, doctrinal, and outmoded, while sweepingly and uncritically accepting the latter. Actually each is in itself an image of reality which has emerged in much the same way—as fruits of the spirit in human community. Both are great and lasting products of the human mind and imagination which are equally intended to make publicly manifest a central aspect of reality in the cosmos as a whole. Yet our age accords to physics a status so objective and unassailable as to be essentially independent of the human mind and imagination, while at the same time it relegates Christianity to the status of a private ethic, subjectively comforting and helpful, but unrelated to anything existing outside the individual Christian.

Fact vs. Faith

Another way in which these two fields are frequently contrasted is the assertion that science is based on facts whereas religion must be taken on faith. Such an assertion is quite as untrue from the standpoint of the basis on fact as it is from that of the dependence on faith. In the first place I can bear witness from my own experience that I had just as much sheer factual material to learn and digest in my preparation for Holy Orders as I did in obtaining my doctorate in physics. The range of subject matter from modern Biblical scholarship, through church history and liturgics, to moral and dogmatic theology represents a most extensive factual base upon which Christianity rests. It requires prolonged and disciplined effort to achieve a thorough grounding in Christianity.

Faith, on the other hand, is just as essential an element of science as it is of Christianity. This is, perhaps, a much more difficult point to grasp adequately than the other. The reason, I believe, is the common misconception of science which regards it as a self-regulating mechanism which automatically produces information when the crank of scientific method is turned. Very little faith would be required, of course, for the operation of such a mechanism. But science, as we have seen, is not at all that kind of affair. The investigator confronting nature directly, finds nothing resembling the smooth, ordered, lawful behavior depicted by the textbooks. What he finds instead is, in Conant's apt phrase, the downright "cussedness of nature." A crucial experiment successfully performed is a major achievement which only fellow scientists who themselves have met nature face to face can fully appreciate. Scientific research is a tough and unrelenting business. Only those who enjoy a firm and unshakable faith in the ultimate intelligibility of the chaotic torrent of phenomena in terms of underlying laws and universal principles can possibly stand up under it and carry through with it successfully. Often students discover when they leave the textbook stage and try to grapple with nature directly that they simply cannot believe that they can derive anything orderly and dependable and sure from their experiments. When this happens all they can do is change fields, and the reason is quite simply a failure of faith. Without such an abiding faith it is simply not possible to become a part of the community. The acquisition of such a faith is the prime requisite for the process of incorporation into the science community which we described earlier.

It is a mistake to think of apparatus smoothly grinding out data in accordance with the regularity and dependability of natural law. Apparatus in general simply does not work that way. Instead, what comes out of it most of the time is a mess; unrepeatable, often quixotic, frequently baffling and frustrating. The common experience with apparatus is that of something under the control of gremlins bent on defeating the experimenter rather than ruled by invariable and smoothly functioning natural laws. The inexperienced may even develop a psychological block against making a run on even very fine equipment for fear that it will not really work for them. There is nothing confident or lighthearted about their approach to an experiment. Instead, gnawing doubts that any kind of dependable and repeatable regularity will ever emerge for them from their data assail and unnerve them. No matter how thorough their factual knowledge or how expert their technique, if they really do not believe in their bones that underneath the surface turbulence of recorded data there are really discoverable and operative regularities, they cannot do physics. The gift of such a belief, however, is a matter of faith, not of knowledge or skill.

By contrast there is a wonderfully inspiring quality about the really competent investigator in the sure and confident way in which he can throw a piece of apparatus together, get the bugs out of it with an intuitive feel for them of the most extraordinary sort, and in due time have it working and giving data which surely reveals hidden and unsuspected regularities in nature. He is lighthearted and confident about his work and can approach the laboratory with an air of sure mastery which is wonderful to behold. Even he, however, may on occasion also experience long stretches of bewildering and frustrating results from which nothing sure or dependable emerges. The annals of science are filled with stories of such frustration among even its greatest figures. In such an extended period of continuous frustration and despair, the reality and primacy of the faith on which the successful pursuit of science depends becomes abundantly evident. The scientist has to really believe in his bones that the world must be made in a certain way, in spite of overwhelming evidence to the contrary, in order to find the strength and the courage to keep going. The faith on which such confidence rests is clearly a gift which others may catch from him as they would an infection, but which otherwise cannot in any way be mechanically taught as one might teach a subject or a technique. But this is precisely the reason why physics is in its essence much more a community than it is a subject.

Much the same situation prevails with that community of the faithful in Christ called the Church. The world as we experience it directly does not seem at all the kind of world which the Christian God would create and govern. In the torrent of events in which we are all caught up, there is such a mixture of evil, misery, cruelty, and injustice that disbelief in the Christian assertions about the nature of the reality which lies at the heart of all events is easy. Yet here, too, faith in the God of goodness, mercy, and love—and of wrath and judgment also—who has revealed himself in Christ, is the prime requisite for incorporation into the Christian community. To those within this community who have been given such a faith, the world takes on a different aspect and is seen with new eyes. It provides them with a firm foundation on which to stand and a fresh vantage point from which to look out upon events. They receive through the gift of this faith the courage to keep going in the face of repeated evidence contrary to their belief, as well as the power to find and respond to the reality of Christ in events which for others are merely chaotic and meaningless. There is an important parallel here. The faith which is essential to the fruitful pursuit of scientific inquiry endows those who share it with the power to uncover and make manifest an underlying order and regularity beneath the surface turbulence of events by which these events are seen to be subject to the rule of universal laws. In the same way the faith which is essential to the fruitful pursuit of the Christian life endows those who share it with the power to know and respond to the hand of God operative behind the same surface turbulence of events by which these events are seen to be subject to the rule of his providence and judgment.

The difficulty is that the nature of faith in both science and Christianity is widely misunderstood. Faith as applied to either is frequently thought of as a set of propositional statements to which an unquestioning verbal assent is demanded. Such propositions in both are, however, properly the subject of doctrine rather than faith. Both physics and Christianity have a well-formulated set of doctrines to which the faithful in each give general assent. In both cases such doctrines represent the end result of protracted and difficult ventures in understanding, and the respective communities, quite properly and understandably, cling to them tenaciously. Few people outside the community of physics realize how strongly those within the community hold to the present set of doctrines which characterize modern physics, nor how essential it is to the preservation of any kind of stability in the enterprise of physics that what has been gained with such great labor and agony of spirit be not lightly relinquished. On the other hand, few people outside the Church realize how much it is possible in principle to modify essentially all of the historic doctrines of the Catholic faith, nor how essential it is to the power and vitality of the Gospel that each age re-express the historic understandings of the Faith in the light of its own experience. The trouble with doctrine in contemporary physics is that everyone on the outside supposes it to be easily changed, but very few on the inside have the genius and courage to attempt it. The trouble in Christian theology is just the reverse. There everyone on the outside supposes the doctrines to be rigorously and permanently fixed, while those on the inside are often too easily tempted to advance naïve proposals for radical changes without a proper appreciation of the extent to which the suggested change has been thoroughly explored and rejected long ago.

In either case, however, doctrine is not the equivalent of faith. Faith in physics, as we have just seen, does not consist in an adherence to any particular set of propositions about the nature of physical reality, but rather in an ingrained conviction concerning the ultimate intelligibility of any phenomenon in terms of universal natural laws. In exactly the same way, faith in Christianity does not consist in the adherence to any particular set of historic doctrines, but in an ingrained belief in Christ as the incarnate Son of God, and in the reality of God as revealed in him. In either case faith is quite distinct from doctrine. Moreover, when properly understood, the distinction is one which holds with equal force and equal primacy in both physics and Christianity. The contrast so frequently made between these two fields which regards science as based on fact and reason, without involving faith, while considering religion to be based on faith alone, without recourse to fact and reason, is entirely fallacious and misleading.

Impersonal *vs.* Personal Knowledge

Another way in which science and religion are frequently contrasted is in terms of the personal and impersonal. This contrast is based on the belief that science is a dispassionate, completely detached activity in which the process of knowing is independent of the involvement or participation of the knower. In contrast to this, religious knowledge is deeply personal since it comes only through the passionate involvement and commitment of the believer in that which he knows. This widely held opinion is not, however, borne out at all in my own experience. As I look back over my own career and try to compare in these terms my entry into and activity in physics with my subsequent entry into and activity in the Church, I cannot identify any such sharp contrast between the impersonal in the one and the personal in the other. What is true instead is that I was deeply involved in physics, personally committed to it, and passionately devoted to its pursuit. Moreover, I am convinced that such knowledge of physics as I was able to acquire came only as a result of this personal involvement. To me physics and Christianity seem equally personal because everything I know in either has come about in much the same way through my own passionate involvement in, and personal commitment to, each. Nor does this seem to be any merely individual peculiarity. When I consider my colleagues in both fields, I cannot see that physics is any less personal for my fellow physicists than is Christianity for my fellow clergy.

A bit of personal biography from the distinguished physicist Werner Heisenberg is relevant here. In a recent magazine article he describes how outraged he was by diagrams in his high school physics text which attempted to explain molecular valence by showing atoms with hooks and eyes. Later on, in the university, he discussed his disturbance with a friend who, it turned out, did not share it, but rather defended such complicated diagrams of atoms and asserted that someday a supermicroscope would be built, one employing perhaps gamma rays in place of visible light, which would make all such detailed structures of atoms visible. Heisenberg says of this conversation, "This argument disquieted me deeply. I was afraid that this imaginary microscope might well reveal the hooks and eyes of my physics textbook, and once again I had to resolve the apparent contradiction between this proposed experiment and the basic conceptions of Greek philosophy." It was precisely out of this sense of personal threat and deep inner disturbance that Heisenberg committed himself to the task which led him later, through an analysis of the operation of a gamma ray microscope, to the discovery of his famous Uncertainty Principle.

This is hardly an instance of the dispassionate, detached, and impersonal relationship to knowledge which is supposed to characterize all scientific work. Yet it is typical of the stories which lie behind the great majority of all the great discoveries in science. In looking backward toward the source of his own insights and knowledge in physics, Heisenberg concludes:

What is and always has been our mainspring is faith. . . . To have faith always means: I decide to do it, I stake my existence on it. When Columbus started on his first voyage into the West, he believed that the earth was round and small enough to be circumnavigated. He did not merely think this was right in theory—he staked his whole existence on it. In a recent discussion of this aspect of European history Freyer has rightly referred to the old saying: *Credo ut intelligam*—"I believe in order that I may understand." In applying this idea to the voyages of discovery, Freyer introduced an intermediate term: *Credo ut agam; ago ut intelligam*—"I believe in order that I may act; I act in order that I may understand." This saying is relevant not only to the first great voyages, but to the whole of Western science, and to the whole mission of the West. (*Harper's,* May 1958.)

This whole question has been exhaustively and decisively dealt with in a recent book by the physical chemist Michael Polanyi. Bearing the title, *Personal Knowledge*, this book is a detailed analysis of just the misconception about the nature of science which we are now considering. The case against the prevalent disassociation of the knower from the known in science is built up meticulously, thoroughly, and with complete competence. It is an important book, long overdue, and should be read by all who still believe that a scientist's personal participation in his knowledge, both in its discovery and in its validation, is not an integral part of science itself. In a partial summary of his thesis, he defines what is meant by the title of his book in a passage which could equally well be applied to Christian knowledge:

Other areas of science will illustrate even more effectively these indispensable intellectual powers, and their passionate participation in the act of knowing. It is to these powers and to this participation that I am referring in the title of this book as "Personal Knowledge." We shall find Personal Knowledge manifested in the appreciation of probability and of order in the exact sciences, and see it at work even more extensively in the way the descriptive sciences rely on skills and connoisseurship. At all these points the act of knowing includes an appraisal; and this personal coefficient, which shapes all factual knowledge, bridges in doing so the disjunction between subjectivity and objectivity. It implies the claim that man can transcend his own subjectivity by striving passionately to fulfill his personal obligations to universal standards. (page 17)

Orthodoxy vs. Heresy

In Dean Schilling's description of the characteristics of the science community his assertion that this community has its own creeds and beliefs, orthodoxies and heresies, is one which I have found causes great resentment and consternation. Let us see in what way his assertion is true of science. In my own field of physics it is a common experience to receive privately published papers which develop all kinds of strange and bizarre theories about everything from electrons and atoms to proofs that Einstein was wrong. When I was a professor at the University of Tennessee, the department kept such communications in a "quack file." To the non-physicist they have as bona fide a ring as a paper in the *Physical Review*. But to physicists they are immediately recognized as fundamentally different. They constitute in the strict sense of the word unorthodox or heretical physics. In subtle ways impossible to describe clearly to the world at large, they violate everything which has given the physics community power to slowly and painfully acquire real and dependable insights into the nature of things. They are lone-wolf efforts unchecked by the discipline of the community and unsupported by an essential loyalty to the enterprise of physics as a whole. Most often the authors of these papers are completely oblivious to these elements and suffer from a deep sense of persecution. They cannot see why their theory has not been given an equal hearing with those of accepted physicists. They cannot understand why the community consistently and repeatedly rejects them.

Orthodoxy and heresy are words which have acquired bad connotations in modern ears. As a result their nature and meaning has been widely misunderstood. Every community must have them in order to be a community at all. Even a street-corner gang has a collection of crucial loyalties, values, beliefs, and standards which represent orthodox behavior for members of the gang. A heretic who fails to share any of these and rebels against the communal requirement of assent to them must be expelled from the gang. If he is not, the gang will soon disintegrate and disperse. So, too, with both science and the Church. There are certain essential attitudes, loyalties, convictions, and devotions without which either community would lose its special source of power, vitality, and integrity. These represent the orthodoxy of the community. These are really crucial to the health and welfare of the community. If it fails to preserve them, it will degenerate into a mere institution or organization, powerless and ineffectual.

Every science has had its heretics. For the most part, as in the case of Christianity, they dry up and disappear being powerless to attract others into their fold. Science is not yet old enough to have produced many heretical offshoots with power to grow into significant schismatic bodies. The Church, however, has had such in its history, although it was only in the fourth, fifth, and sixth centuries, when the Church was already three centuries old, that the great Arian, Nestorian, and Monophysite heresies arose. There are today in science, however, two instances of scientific heretical movements. One is represented by the osteopaths as a schismatic heretical body attached to orthodox medicine, and the other is the science of parapsychology devoted to the investigation of the so-called psi-phenomena which to orthodox psychology is heresy. A study of either of these two contemporary movements can be very illuminating in revealing the true character of heresy in general. For example, the long struggle waged by the osteopaths in state legislatures to achieve legal equality with medical physicians has many parallels in the legislative history of the struggle for religious toleration. In the case of parapsychology, it would be illuminating to those who like to think of science as an impersonal mechanism which automatically follows wherever the evidence takes it, to study the reaction of orthodox psychology to this field of investigation.* A number of leading psychologists in writing on the subject clearly indicate that their objections to telepathy and other psi-phenomena are based on

* A study of the group of articles in the January 6, 1956, issue of *Science* (Vol. 123, pp. 7-20) will be found most instructive in this connection.

something deeper than mere statistical evidence, so that even if the evidence were proved statistically sound and unimpeachable they still would not believe it.

All of this has a bearing on the widespread notion that religion necessarily imposes a rigid strait jacket on the intellect in contrast to science which is intellectually free and unhampered by any authority. In my own experience of incorporation into both communities, such a notion is completely false. In both cases it was necessary, first to accept and willingly conform to the discipline of the community, then to respond to its authority before the community could bestow upon me its power of liberating the intellect to carry out really fruitful inquiry. The tendency is to underrate completely the toughness and difficulty of really fruitful intellectual activity in either science or theology. Without a firm foundation on which to stand, one simply cannot grapple with experience in the tough and sturdy way which is required for real understanding. But such a platform cannot be had apart from the discipline and authority of the community. A completely free intellect operating in a lone and isolated self, cut free from every tie which binds into community, is an impotent thing tossed to and fro by every wind and wave. I could not even begin to do physics until I had given myself fully and freely to physics. Neither could I begin to do theology until I had given myself fully and freely to Christ in his Church.

The authority and discipline which every community exercises over its members represents at once the primary source of its power and vitality and, at the same time, its most fearful danger. When the community is dynamic, vigorous, and full of vitality, its authority and discipline are so gladly and spontaneously accepted by its members that they are scarcely conscious of it. This is the case with science today, and it has been the case with the Church in all of its past periods of greatness. The vitality, genius, and brilliance of the intellectual activity of the Church during the fourth and fifth centuries matches that of theoretical physics in the nineteenth and twentieth. If one wishes to really understand authority, discipline, dogma, and orthodoxy in the Church in a way which brings out their necessary character and fruitfulness, one must study such a period in the Church's life as that.

The nineteenth-century enlightenment had a corrosive effect on the Church and we are just beginning to emerge from the deadness and sterility which resulted. The great difficulty in talking about Christianity today is that it is this nineteenth-century image and vision of the Church, which is predominant in the minds of contemporary audiences. When the power and vitality is sapped out of any community so that there is left behind only an empty institutional shell, the imposition of its authority and discipline, and the maintenance of its dogma and orthodoxy become evil and obnoxious, stultifying the intellect and imprisoning the soul. It is, nevertheless, no solution to simply discard all these elements, for to do so only disintegrates the community leaving it powerless to bestow any powers or capacities at all upon its members.

II

Science and Christianity as Communities

THE IDEA of community is extraordinarily subtle, and it is difficult to define or circumscribe it in a precise way. Few of us are aware of the intimate role which the human communities of which we are a part have played in forming us as persons and making us what we are. Through family and school, team and club, organization and society, we have come to be what we are. Had the communities of which we have been or are a part been quite different, we would ourselves be entirely different persons than we now are. We know the truth of this. Yet, at the same time, we are aware of our independence of these communities, of our struggle to maintain and assert our own individuality against the hold which they have upon us. Between these two facts we find ourselves at a loss to understand the way in which community operates, the true source of its potency, and the proper limits to be placed upon its action.

Even a prison or a reformatory is a community. Speaking of such a community in his Kent School lecture, "The Person in Community," Alan Paton said:

Who is this boy for whom this community exists? We all know what he is. He is an offender; perhaps he stole or robbed or murdered. But for his sake money is poured out like water, buildings are erected, principals, priests, psychologists, teachers, counselors, are all assembled together. Though he is the least of all, all this is done for his sake. Is he in secret the child of someone great, maybe, that it would be a matter of such moment for him to be saved? Who is he indeed?

. . .

It is not only this boy who is the person in community, it is you, it is myself. We are born into the community, and as we grow up we must enter more and more actively into its life. Perhaps when we are thirty, forty, fifty years old, we may decide to become hermits and to live alone. But we cannot do that while we are young. If we were shut off in childhood from the life in community, we would never become persons at all. It would be like shutting off a sapling from the life of the forest; you could build a room about it and shelter it from the heat of the sun, the force of the wind, the cold of the snow, but what kind of tree would it be? (page 102)

Some Methods of Approach to Community Study

In this chapter we shall endeavor to uncover such insights and understandings as can be had into the nature of community and of the person in community. In doing so, however, the primary concern will be with the two communities of science and of Christianity. In many of their aspects they share the same characteristics as community in general. In discussing the communities of science and Christianity, we shall at the same time be gaining insights into community in general. There are, however, some aspects of these two communities which are more or less peculiar to them and are not found in most other communities. For the most part these aspects are related to the fact that both scientific and religious communities are centered around an access to reality which it is their special function to provide. Entrance into the community opens up a new vista of apprehension of reality which is inaccessible apart from the community. Most other human communities do not perform this function in any primary or explicit way. As we proceed we shall single out and take note of these distinguishing characteristics in the two communities. Clearly an adequate treatment of our subject requires that we see both in what ways the two communities share in the nature of community in general, and in what ways they possess distinctive features of their own.

Until the comparatively recent development of the sciences of community—cultural anthropology, social psychology, and sociology—there was very little consideration of the nature of community as a defined and circumscribed object of study. Most people knew intimately only the comparatively few communities of which they were a part. These they took for granted as being so basic and integral to the phenomenon of life that the idea of inquiring into the specific role of community in shaping their own personhood did not occur to them. The extensive labors of the various kinds of social scientists over the past several decades have, however, greatly illuminated this whole subject and placed it in a new perspective. As a result of such studies, we have become aware of the remarkable range and diversity of human communities. Strange and bizarre primitive cultures, very different from anything in our own experience, have been described for us. We have been able to sense something of their inner harmony and power and, by contrast with that which is familiar to us, to see the communities of which we are a part from a new vantage point with a larger and more comprehensive perspective. From all these studies we have also acquired a fresh appreciation for the power and inner dynamics of community in shaping human life and creating the human person. Yet for all this there remains much that is still mysterious and seemingly incapable of precise objective definition. Community remains a subtle thing with inner depths which we have only begun to penetrate, and with intricacies of structure and function of the most delicate and fleeting sort.

The unsuspected perils and extraordinary difficulty of a proper scientific study of community have been brought out with great clarity and precision by the sociologist George Homans, in his book *The Human Group*. Here in a masterly piece of analytical examination, carried out with extreme care to uncover and eliminate all non-scientific subjective judgments, one can gain an appreciation of the severely limited scope of any strictly objective knowledge of community which it seems possible to achieve. Indeed, it seems that the more nearly one approaches the scientific ideal of detached objectivity, the less it is possible to know about the subject of community in any important or relevant sense. What remains are a few rather trivial generalizations which seem far removed from the essential reality of the subject and largely unrelated to the inner source of creative power and life-giving vitality which we are most concerned to understand when we study community.

The dilemma which the student of community faces in his endeavor to translate an "inside view" into an "outside view," conforming with the criteria of science and scholarship for acceptable forms of exposition, have been expressed particularly clearly by the anthropologist Robert Redfield in his book *The Little Community*. The poignancy of the dilemma is made particularly clear in one passage from his discussion of this point:

> If I should come perfectly to share the inside view of the Maya Indian villager, to share all his thoughts and feelings, and yet could state these thoughts and feelings only in his language, in his gesture and act, I should have triumphed over the difficulty of getting the inside view, but of course I should have failed as completely as a scholar and scientist. There was a student of the Zuni Indians years ago, Frank Cushing, who assumed the inside view so perfectly that he became in effect a Zuni Indian and was made, I believe, a Priest of the Bow in their religion. But after that he told outsiders nothing more about the Zuni. (page 82)

Carrying the subtitle, "Viewpoints for the Study of a Human Whole," this fascinating little book presents us with the author's own quest for clarity and understanding in his efforts to find vantage points from which a scientific study of the community as a whole integrated object of investigation could be launched. Unlike Homans' book, which seeks to dissect particular communities in order to analyze them into identifiable basic components universally applicable to all communities, this book seeks to discover fruitful ways for studying particular communities as wholes. It is not systematic and rigidly structured in approach, but rather exploratory, inquiring, and tentative. Much more than any other scientific book in this field with which I am acquainted, I have found it fruitful in understanding my own experience of involvement in community. In particular, it is especially valuable as a guide and source of insight for exploring both science and Christianity as communities. Among the several viewpoints which Redfield explores, at least six are directly applicable to these communities, so that our inquiry can be organized under the same headings which he employs for his more general treatment of all kinds of little communities.

Social Structure

A common way of studying community is in terms of its social structure. Every community involves a system of interpersonal relationships and interactions among its members within which each member has his own particular place, function, role, and status. In time much of this structure may become formalized and concretely established into a definite organizational framework of institutions, offices, officials, and ranks. This organized form of social structure is easy enough to recognize and define but often difficult to evaluate in terms of its role in the actual life and functioning of the community. The more basic form of social structure, involving the actual, though undefined and fluid, fabric of interpersonal relationships by means of which the work of the community is carried on, is much more difficult to recognize and describe but much easier to evaluate in terms of the actual life of the community.

The various science communities are acquiring, as time goes on, more and more of an explicit organized structure. This has been happening to physics at an accelerated pace since the last war, and it had already begun with chemistry after World War I. The great government laboratories, industrial research centers, and over-sized university departments are heavily organized in graded hierarchies of offices and positions, running from the laboratory director down to the technician. The American Physical Society acquires more and more formal organizational structure every year. As physics grows and matures, so do the institutions and offices which the increasing complexity of the enterprise requires grow with it. Each new generation of physicists finds itself working in a more institutionalized and organized framework than did the last.

It is not, however, in formal organization that the essential social structure of any science is to be found. Rather must we look to the wholly unformalized structure of interpersonal dependence, stimulation, and restraint which from the beginning has been an essential feature of the actual operation of a science. Too often science is thought of only in terms of its great masters as though it were made up of a series of individual contributions. In such a view physics, for example, would be typified by such names as Newton, Maxwell, Einstein, Bohr, and Heisenberg. That view, however, gives a completely distorted understanding not only of what physics is but of the way in which its achievements have been attained. One has to know, too, of the ordinary scientists, those mostly unknown except to contemporaries in their own narrow fields, as well as those who serve them, the technicians, shop men, and secretaries. In its actual functioning physics is the product of the complex interplay in mutual dependence and stimulation of a great variety of persons of widely varying capacities, skills, interests, and aptitudes. There is experimental and theoretical physics, the physics of the frontier where new discoveries are made and the physics of the interior where slow, painstaking work is done, and there is applied physics and so-called fundamental physics. Everyone who has participated in the science enterprise knows how essential this whole structure of persons is to it, and how unthinkable the great masters with their contributions and insights would be apart from it.

One of the great figures of contemporary physics, J. Robert Oppenheimer, has expressed this point in a passage of eloquence and power which, I am confident, would receive the immediate and spontaneous assent of any physicist who reads it. The passage is from his Reith lectures, which have been published under the title, *Science and the Common Understanding*:

> Each of us knows from his own life how much even a casual and limited association of men goes beyond him in knowledge, in understanding, in humanity, and in power. Each of us, from a friend or a book or by concerting of the little we know with what others know, has broken the iron circle of his frustration. Each of us has asked help and been given it, and within our measure each of us has offered it. Each of us knows the great new freedom sensed almost as a miracle, that men banded together for some finite purpose experience from the power of their common effort. . . . Each of us knows how much he has been transcended by the group of which he has been or is a part; each of us has felt the solace of other men's knowledge to stay his own ignorance, of other men's wisdom to stay his folly, of other men's courage to answer his doubts or his weakness. (page 91f.)

It is, of course, essentially the same with the other community with which we are particularly concerned here, the Church. We need only note in passing that the Church, too, has acquired a formal organization and structure which, over its much longer time span, has become much more institutionalized and formalized as well as more complex than that of science. But here, too, it is really the informal network of social structure to which we must look in order to find its essential character of community manifested. The Church is and always has been an ordered structure of widely ranging relationships, roles, and status among its members, requiring "a diversity of gifts from the one Spirit." If we were to know it only, as sometimes happens, in terms of its great bishops, teachers, prophets, and saints, we would really not know it properly or adequately. As Saint Paul says, "If the whole body were an eye, where would be the hearing?" For those within the Church, it is the common life in the Body of

Christ, in which each member is fitly joined together with every other, which constitutes its essence and its redemptive power. Indeed the passage just quoted from Oppenheimer could without modification be taken over in its entirety as a vivid and accurate description of life within the Church as attested to by the faithful in any age.

A Typical Biography

Another of Redfield's approaches to understanding a community as a human whole consists in identifying and constructing a typical biography of one who passes through the community and is formed by it. Any stable community is a lasting thing. Men and women are born into it or enter it in later life, pass through it, and move out of it at death. Within the community they are profoundly affected by its spirit, caught up in the stream of its life, nourished and sustained by its power, and given a degree of personal fulfillment within its embrace. To describe a characteristic passage through a community by means of a typical biography of an individual in that community is certainly a very relevant way to study the community as a whole.

In the case of the Church this is, of course, a very common way of exhibiting and making evident what the Church really is. Much of Saint Paul's writing is biographical and certainly the vast majority of his insights into the nature of the Church are derived directly in terms of his own passage through it. The *Confessions* of Saint Augustine continue to occupy the primary place among his writings, as providing the most direct and illuminating view of the nature of the Church as he knew it. So, too, with numerous other Christian biographies and autobiographies throughout the intervening centuries. In each of them we are, so to speak, conducted on a temporal tour through the Church. Along the way we come to see and understand what the life of grace in Christ is really like, how such a life responds to the sacramental nurture of the Church, and in what way the community operates to provide such a life with inner resources of courage, strength, and joy. Through such biography we are also enabled to look out upon the world from the vantage point of one within the community and thereby to make manifest something of the knowledge of reality which has been revealed through the community. The Church has always maintained that its most effective means of communication was that of personal witness. This, however, is essentially equivalent to a representation of the Church by means of a typical biography of one of its members.

In science the use of the typical biography is not nearly so common a way of expressing what science itself is. This, however, is much more a defect than it is a virtue. Now that it is becoming increasingly important for scientists to communicate to the general public an appreciation of science as it really is, the biographical method is being used more and more for the task. Much of the public misunderstanding of science is the result of a dearth of personal testimonials about the experience of engaging in science. Such a novel as C. P. Snow's *The Search* or a book like Arthur Compton's *Atomic Quest* can go far toward dispelling such misunderstanding.

In my case the only really effective way I have found when called upon to answer the insistently recurring question about the compatibility of science and religion is to refer to biography. An example of my approach along these lines is provided in the previous chapter in which the discussion is primarily biographical throughout in the sense that it deals exclusively with the experience of persons involved in either physics or Christianity as opposed to subject matter. Although what is asked for and expected is generally an answer dealing with subject matter, I believe that the deeper reason behind such questions is the unrecognized conviction that people have deep down inside them that the real basis for reconciling the truth of science with the truth of Christianity is not really philosophical or metaphysical, but personal. No amount of intercomparison of subject matter can substitute for a person on whom both the communities of physics and the Christian Church have operated with unreserved and unrestricted power.

People sense without realizing it that the real key to the problem is to be found in a person who has been fully incorporated into both communities, who has committed himself to each without reservation and who has shared to the full the life and power and spirit of each of them. This is also clear evidence of the extent to which we all rely on typical biography as a means for understanding community.

The Kind of Person

Closely related to the characterization of a community by means of a typical biography of a community member is characterization in terms of the kind of person it produces, both actually and ideally. Persons are formed in community, and it is the chief power and function of community to bring forth and create personhood in its members. Because of this the study of a community in terms of the kind of person it is supposed to produce as well as the kind it actually produces represents a basic approach to an understanding of the community. An anthropologist writing about a primitive culture will often begin with a character or personality sketch of the kind of people who make up the culture, their moods and interests, whether they are happy or morose, peaceful or contentious, lethargic or active. Although individual variations are recognized, the objective is to picture the whole community as though it were a single personality. The widespread use of this approach is indicative of its relevance to the idea of community. The more we know about the kind of persons who make up a community, the more we feel we have come to know the community itself. On the other hand, no approach to the study of a community is more difficult to carry out along scientifically acceptable lines than this one.

Now the communities of physics and Christianity can each be characterized in terms of a kind of person. This, perhaps, is more immediately obvious in the case of the Church than it is in the case of science. The most common way in which people in general evaluate and judge the Church is in terms of the kind of people who make up the community of Christians. By contrast the various sciences are not commonly characterized so much by the kind of people who engage in them as by their subject matter and practical achievements. Both the excessive overemphasis on the kind of person in the one case and the excessive underemphasis in the other constitute distortions which are not only misleading but the source of many widespread misconceptions of both Christianity and science.

The importance of a shift of emphasis in science from subject matter and things to the persons involved in it has been highlighted by the current concern in this country over the inadequate number of students who are attracted to careers in science. In the extensive consideration which this problem has been receiving the root of the difficulty is often identified as lying in the distorted image of the scientist as a person which results from the way in which science is taught in our secondary schools. The character of this image among high school students was recently made the object of a large-scale study by the American Association for the Advancement of Science. The report on the results of this study by Margaret Mead and Rhoda Métraux gives a detailed characterization of the kind of person high school students believe a scientist to be. What is conspicuously absent in this characterization is any sense of the extent to which imagination, intellectual delight, excitement, and adventure enter into the scientific enterprise. Also lacking is any sense of the community of science and of the rewarding interpersonal relationships and human involvements which enter into it. One is struck by the contrast between the kinds of persons which scientists know themselves to be, and the image of this kind of person which is being formed in the minds of our young people. Apart from this primary objective of the study, however, a secondary result of it has been to point up how vital it is to recognize explicitly that each science is, in its essence, a human community made up of a distinctive kind of person, and that the reasons for the very existence of each science as a component of our culture are essentially human reasons.

The contrast which has just been noted between the inside and outside views of what kind of person a scientist is occurs equally sharply in the case of Christianity. I have often been struck by the similarity of the problem I face in trying, on the one hand, to express to the outside world what it is like to be a physicist and engage in the enterprise of physics as I have known and experienced it and, on the other hand, to try to express to those who have not really known or experienced it what it is like to be a Christian and participate in the power of the Christian life. Here, too, the prevailing image of the Christian in the minds of those outside the historic Catholic Church is generally as distorted and uninviting as is the prevailing image of the scientist in the minds of those outside science. This observation reinforces the problem which is Redfield's chief concern in his chapter under this title; namely, the extraordinary difficulty of achieving an adequate objective representation of any community in terms of the kind of persons who make it up.

Outlook on Life

The little communities of relatively self-contained primitive cultures which Redfield and other anthropologists study provide for their members a view of the universe and of man's place in the scheme of things. One approach to the study of such a community is through the world view which it provides for its members. One approaches the characterization of a Maya village, say, by asking what the universe looks like to one of the villagers. What is the nature of the image of reality which he holds in his mind, and what conceptions does he have of the meaning of life, the theme of history, and his own place and significance in it all? The more nearly one can approach an understanding of the whole of this outlook on life which its members share, the more one will understand of the community itself as a human whole. It is briefly this which Redfield has in mind when he speaks of the "world-view" approach to a study of communities.

When we apply to our own complex civilization and the multitude of interwoven communal associations which make it up, this method of study, we find that it is not applicable to the great majority of communities in our culture. For most of the communities which flourish in our culture have little in the way of a world view as a distinctive element of their common life, because in our culture the transmission of a world view is largely confined to the two communities which are our particular concern here, science and religion. What the self-contained little community itself furnishes in a primitive culture, these two great corporate responses of the human spirit to the realities about us perform in the civilized culture of the West. Thus this particular pathway to an understanding of community in general (which Redfield explores) is uniquely suited to the particular kind of community in which we are interested here.

The primary fact about the world view of western man is the tension in which he stands between two images of the world which present him with radically contrasting views of reality. On the one hand, there is the powerfully formative Judeo-Christian tradition of western culture, preserved and transmitted down through the ages by the Church. On the other, is the classical Graeco-Roman tradition which during the last three centuries has flowered into the vast panorama of modern science. Each of these constitutes a view of the universe and of man's place in it which is held in community with all the loyalty, belief, and commitment which the maintenance of any vital and living community demands. Each tradition opens up to those who share its life a vision of reality and an understanding of the nature and scheme of things which joins together into a valid whole great ranges of experience which would otherwise be chaotic and unintelligible. Yet the two ranges of experience, as well as the character of the reality which unifies them, are radically different in these two roots of our culture. In this difference lies the root of what has always been a fundamental tension in western culture.

The world view of our Judeo-Christian heritage has always been explicitly known and transmitted through a well-defined and constituted community of response and witness. It consists of a total view of reality which can best be identified as the Biblical view. The whole complex of understandings of God, man, and nature which make up the Biblical view of reality were known initially to a community, Israel, through the intimacy of a uniquely close relationship with God represented by the word "covenant." This relationship has been fulfilled and inherited through Christ by a new community, the Church, through a new covenant. It is an essential element of the Biblical view of reality that the truth and power of the knowledge of God, man, and the world revealed through it can be known only within the community where it is taught by the Holy Spirit, and by means of which witness to it is borne from one generation to another. The truth of this assertion has been somewhat obscured in the last few centuries by a number of developments. Among these we may cite, first, the tendency to make religion a private individual affair in which the truth of Christianity is unrelated to the community in Christ; second, the reaction against any form of doctrine or dogma with the result that Christianity becomes reduced from a true world view to a mere ethical and moral standard; and, third, fundamentalist views of the Bible which make words and propositions ultimate and reduce the holy communities of Israel and the Church to a secondary dependent status. Such distortions are, however, relatively recent and temporary, as well as alien to the Biblical view of reality itself. In that view the covenant community—the virgin of Israel, the chosen people, the Bride of Christ, the household of God—is the central and essential element in the whole knowledge of reality which it represents.

In the case of science the role of community is equally central to the knowledge of reality which it has achieved. This fact, however, is not generally recognized. There is in science nothing comparable to Israel or the Church with which the world view of science is explicitly connected as is the case with the Biblical world view. Yet, as has already been clarified to some extent and will be further explained in what follows, the relationship between scientific knowledge and the community of science is just as crucial and essential as it is in the case of the Judeo-Christian knowledge of reality. In the three centuries since Newton the human communal enterprise which we designate as physics has been engaged in constructing an ever more detailed, comprehensive, and extended image of the physical structure of the natural world. What has been achieved is an already beautifully unified and coherent conceptual scheme which certainly stands as one of the most exalted achievements of human intelligence and imagination which man has ever made. This achievement cannot, however, be attributed to any one person or sequence of isolated individual investigators. Quite clearly, this achievement has been possible only because there came into existence a community of men, charged with high hopes and an unshakable belief in the fertility of their enterprise, empowered by an indomitable spirit, and filled with a vitality and dynamism which has carried the enterprise forward with unbroken success and achievement. Without this community physics as we know it now would be unthinkable. Moreover, anyone who desires to share fully for himself the complete image of reality which physics has achieved can do so only, as we have already seen, by becoming a full member of this community. Just as with the world view of any other community, the knowledge of the structure of physical reality which physics now possesses is an "inside view" which those on the outside simply cannot know in any but superficial and inadequate ways. The knowledge of reality in each of the sciences is an image of the world which has been acquired and is possessed in community, just as much as the knowledge which is held and witnessed in the Church is an access to reality which has been given and can be known only in community.

Such questions as the differences in the kind of knowledge which is held in these two communities, the different bases for our confidence in the validity of such knowledge, or the extent to which in each case what is held can properly be said to be known, are all matters to be dealt with in subsequent chapters. What is desired here is simply to point up the intimate and necessary connection between knowledge and community in each case. Just as in a self-contained primitive culture the world view or image of reality which is held within the culture is so intimately a part of the community that this alone can be taken as a vantage point from which to study the community as a whole, so too in our much more complex western culture the images of reality which Christianity and science have given us are intimately tied up with the corresponding communities. Here, too, the relationship is so close and of such an essential character that an understanding of either Christianity or science as communal entities within western culture can be had, along with the other ways which Redfield explores, by considering each of them in terms of the outlook on life which it is the special province of each to preserve and transmit.

History

Another quite different approach to the study of a community which Redfield explores is that of concentrating one's attention on its history. In opening up this route of inquiry he does not intend to take over for this purpose all aspects of history and historiography which are associated with the whole field of inquiry and scholarship represented by these words. Rather he proceeds by narrowing down what is to be meant by history or a historical approach until what remains is directly applicable to an understanding of a little community as a whole. His approach is best understood in terms of a series of questions which he raises:

> . . . if one begins with a desire to understand a community of living people as a whole, what historiography of that community will contribute to our understanding of it as a whole? We have seen that our whole is many kinds of whole. Of the kinds of wholes we have considered in looking at the contemporary community, which can enter into the history we write of it? What account of what arrangements of events will have relevance to our understanding of the community . . . as social structure, a characteristic kind of person . . . or as outlook on life? Or in the writing of a history of a little community, shall we discover new kinds of wholenesses, or perhaps

find that the kinds of wholenesses we thought we saw in its present life disappear as we write the account of the events which led up to its present? (page 98)

The relevance of posing these same questions with respect to both Christianity and a science like physics is obvious. Indeed, in both cases, the importance of history in gaining an appreciation and understanding of the community is already established. In theological education church history occupies a place of importance second only to that of Holy Scripture—which is itself a history of the community throughout the period during which the process of revelation was being enacted. Only from a study of the history of the Church can an appreciation of its greatness and potentiality be gained. It is much the same in science too, although, doubtless as a result of the relative youth of science, courses in the history of science are not commonly taught as such. Actually, however, all teaching in physics has a historical character, and much of the actual historical process by which the present insights and understandings were gained necessarily emerges in any method of teaching them as they are presently known. Ideas emerge out of a particular context, and in order to understand the idea, it is necessary to have some appreciation of the setting out of which it arose. New discoveries and key advances are not made in a vacuum, but always in response to a problem. In order to understand them one must see clearly what the nature of the problem was. In order to do that, however, one must reconstruct, at least partially, the state of physics within which the problem arose. In this way the process of learning physics inevitably involves at least some degree of familiarity with the history of physics.

In the effort to understand the Church as community the vantage point of history is uniquely suitable as compared with other communities. The reason for this is that its total insight into reality, the entire body of revealed truth to which it bears witness, is, in an essential way, exclusively based in history. Whereas science deals with repeatable events which manifest timeless universal aspects of reality, Christianity is based on meanings inherent in singular non-recurring events in history. The key element in Christianity in the light of which everything else is to be understood is found in a sequence of unique events in the real history of this world through which, within a covenant community, God has revealed himself in action as creator and redeemer, punisher and rescuer, judge and savior. The image of reality which Christianity provides for those within the community for the faithful is thus solidly grounded in history. This makes an understanding of the history of the community peculiarly relevant to an understanding of the community itself.

The approach through history to an understanding of the deeper things of the Church is especially important to those of us within the Anglican Communion. In an age when the Body of Christ has been so broken and fragmented into a multitude of alienated sub-communities, it is essential to turn to history in order to capture a vision of the integrity, power, and majesty of the Church. In that way we can see how the purity of the Catholic faith, the clarity of the Apostolic witness, and the means of sacramental grace have been protected and preserved through all the changes and chances of her long journey through time. We need to apprehend the continuity of our ministry with that of the Catholic Church in all ages, the identity of the Orders which we possess with those received by our brethren in former times, and the unity of the sacraments which now nourish us with the means by which the Church has always imparted grace to her members. By means of history, too, we are enabled to grasp something of the potentiality of the Church to enter into human life in all sorts of contexts with power to lift, transform, redeem, and ennoble it. Only through glimpsing a vision of this power can such potentialities in our own context be actualized. For most of the Reformation churches and all of the multitudinous Protestant sects this sense of historic continuity and catholicity is not important. But for Anglicans, in common with the Roman Catholic and Orthodox Catholic churches, it is essential to the wholeness of the Faith that the Church be ecumenical vertically in time, as well as horizontally in space in our age or any age to come. For the achievement of any such ecumenicity, however, the heart of the meaning and validity of the community is revealed in and through its history.

Because of the character of the image of reality which it seeks to construct, the science community is not dependent on its history in the same way or to the extent that the Church is. The validity of a scientific theory is in no way dependent on the historical process which produced it. The aim of physics is the discovery of timeless universal laws and structures which underlie and give coherence to the physical universe. Whenever it succeeds in this task, the sequence of events and developments which precede the discovery in no way affect the validity of the final result. Because of the timeless and universal character of the content of science, history has no essential or necessary role to play in it. This circumstance leads to one of the most fundamental differences between science and Christianity. The content of Christianity and the range of reality to which it gives access is essentially and necessarily historical so that the world view of the community is intimately bound up with the history of the community. In the case of science, on the other hand, its content and the range of reality to which it provides access is precisely that part of reality which is always the same so that the world view of science is entirely independent of the history of the community.

This is not to say, however, that history is unimportant to science. On the contrary, in terms of the nature of the scientific enterprise itself, the source of its vitality and power, and the basis for its confidence in the potentiality and fruitfulness of the enterprise, history has primary importance. Wholly apart from its content or results, the enterprise of science as a human endeavor is a major phenomenon of world history. Just a few centuries ago there was no such thing as science in its modern sense as an element of culture. Science and technology, as defined modes of inquiry and application, had been present as far back as we can go in human history. We speak of Babylonian, Egyptian, or Greek science and are able to recognize some degree of scientific activity in almost all cultures and in every epoch. But not until the mid-seventeenth century did anything comparable to science as we know it today come into being. With the founding of the Royal Society in London in 1660 and the French Academy in 1666, explicit and formal recognition was given to the fact that there had come into existence in western culture a new element which, as we know now, was destined to radically transform that culture with a power and decisiveness whose only other parallel in the history of the West is the birth of the Christian Church sixteen centuries earlier. This new element was a community of men bound together for a common quest. It was a community which thereafter would grow continuously with gathering power and momentum, drawing more and more persons into its life and discipline with each new generation. From the beginning this community was charged with a sense of high adventure, confident of the inherent and inevitable fruitfulness of its approach, convinced beyond question of the validity and power of its methodology. There was a kind of Pentecost in the seventeenth century which brought this science community into being, and now, after three centuries of gestation, it has come to full flower and taken over the civilization within which it was conceived, in much the same way as the Church, after its gestation period of three centuries, came to full flower and under Constantine took over the civilization within which it was conceived.

Recently a group of humanists undertook an intensive study of the humanistic aspects of science. The group was under the chairmanship of Harcourt Brown and was made up of "individuals who are not practising or professional scientists but who have been interested in scientific investigation as a human and social phenomenon and who, working from humane studies, are concerned with developing a better understanding of the role and functioning of science in human history." The results of this study have been published under the title, *Science and the Creative Spirit*. This book has much to offer in illuminating our present concern with science as community rather than subject matter. In his essay on science and the literary culture of France, Harcourt Brown says of this community at its inception:

Seventeenth-century physics was no narrow specialized technical study; pursued in the light of important historical perspectives, free from institutional habits and customs, it offered chiefly a challenge to the ingenuity and persistence of the active amateur. As yet it led to no career, and it brought nothing but satisfaction of knowing something new for which it was often difficult to envisage any particular use. . . . As different minds turned towards it, there grew up a clearer sense of a boundless frontier to be explored, and of the dependence of the individual worker on the resources and good will of an ever enlarging circle of like-minded friends. . . . To discover a principle that seemed to govern the behavior of . . . common materials and objects was his delight, and as these principles became more and more consistent, extending towards one another to become laws of nature, and weaving back by inventions into the habits of the trades, the fascination of the scientific quest could only grow. (page 94)

A physicist today when he turns his attention from the electrons, atoms, or molecules which are the objects of his investigation to the people who are engaged with him in the enterprise of carrying out these investigations is likely to become concerned with the history of this community of which he is a part. The subject matter of physics is timeless and passionless. But this subject matter has been discovered bit by bit and slowly woven together into an image of reality by men like himself, who at a certain point in their lives were drawn by the fascination of this enterprise, just as he had been drawn to it, and had given their energies, their devotion, and the commitment of their lives to it, as he has done. These persons, generation after generation, with their common commitment of their lives and fortunes to the common quest of physics, form a community with a history. To explore through its history the way in which this community came into being, the power and dynamism of its growth, the aspirations, delights, and confidence which nourish it, is to understand something of the inner character of the enterprise and why it is worth committing one's life to it. In this way one begins to see oneself as a part of a human whole and to derive insight and understanding of one's own work within this whole from the appreciation of how others have carried out their work within it. This is to see physics as community rather than subject, and when seen that way, its history is a very illuminating route to an understanding of it.

Community within Communities

The last approach, suggested by Redfield with relevance to science and Christianity as communities, which we shall explore, consists in recognizing that every community interacts with, and is partially contained within, other communities. The village is a part of the tribe which, in turn, is a part of a people; and this complex of village, tribe, and people interacts with other tribes and peoples. Each of us is a member of several different communal associations, and these overlapping communities each play their part in shaping us. This question then arises, which Redfield frames thus:

> How in describing the little community, are we to include the fact that it is a community within communities, a whole within other wholes? . . . . What forms of thought are available to us for conceiving and describing a whole that is both inclosed within other wholes and is also in some part permeated by them?" (page 114)

It is clear that both science and Christianity of necessity overlap and interpenetrate other communities. Neither is localized in a particular place. Every scientist lives among, and has relationships and associations with, non-scientists; in like manner the Christian has daily associations with non-Christians. In considering these interrelationships of science or of Christianity with other communities as I have known them in my own experience, I have been struck by one aspect which they have in common which no other community shares with them. This is their world-wide, international character. Both are centered on a reality external to man and his interests, and as such can command the loyalty of persons of every race and national origin. Each spans every boundary of language, state, nation, custom, or culture which constitutes a barrier between other communities of men. In this characteristic they are unique today among every other kind of community in the West of which one may be a part.

This fact about these two communities of which I am so intimately a part has been forcefully brought home to me through two trips which I have made in the last few years, one to Japan and the other to Poland. In each case I was struck by the possibility of enjoying immediately the closest kind of fellowship on terms of real intimacy and quite natural mutuality whenever I was with either another physicist or another Christian, especially a fellow priest of my own Communion. On such travels one is constantly aware of the difference in language, custom, cultural heritage, and national loyalties which separate him from other peoples. In such an environment and in the context of such an experience, the reality and power of the community of physics and of the community of the faithful in Christ is brought home with great force. If one were asked whether this were so without having experienced it, one would say of course of either physics or Christianity that it was world-wide and international. But this is not the same as discovering for oneself how truly and deeply the members of these communities belong to one another and share a common life even though they have never met before and come from widely different backgrounds.

I have been impressed with the testimony of others to this same experience. A number of my colleagues at Oak Ridge attended the International Conference on Peaceful Uses of Atomic Energy in Geneva, Switzerland, in 1955 and again in 1958. All of them give testimony to the wonder of the experience of unity and fellowship in a common endeavor which is actualized in such a conference among scientists of all nations, even among those between whom otherwise the gravest enmity and alienation exists. I have been struck by the similarity of this testimony of my scientific colleagues, to that which I have had simultaneously from a number of bishops who attended the Lambeth Conference in the summer of 1958. This testimony is expressed particularly well in the opening paragraph of the Pastoral Letter from the House of Bishops following that experience:

This letter is written against the background of our unforgettable experience at the recent Lambeth Conference. For forty days we had once again the privilege of meeting with Bishops of the Anglican Communion from many parts of the world. We came from every continent, were members of every race and many nations, and revealed in our fellowship not only the encouraging growth of our own Communion, but also that it is part of the Holy Catholic Church which includes members of every race and nation. We saw anew, against the background of the world's terrible divisions, the oneness of mankind in Christ; we saw that 'in Christ there is no East or West'; we saw that only a world body, freed from the passions and enmities that divide men, can bring a healing and reconciling word to our world. The Lambeth Conference was a symbol of that unity toward which the whole world groans and travails.

The eminent German physicist, Werner Heisenberg, addressing the students of Göttingen University just after the last war on the subject "Science and International Understanding," gave strikingly similar testimony about the science community. Speaking of his experience as a young man working at Bohr's laboratory in Copenhagen, he said:

There I came into a circle of young people of the most diverse nationalities—English, American, Swedish, Norwegian, Dutch, Japanese—all of whom wanted to work on the same problem, Bohr's atomic theory. They nearly always joined together like a big family for excursions, games, social gatherings and sports. In this circle of physicists I had the opportunity of really getting to know people from other nations and their ways of thought. (page 111)

And elsewhere he said:

These conversations left a deep impression on me. First, I learnt that when trying to understand atomic structure it was obviously quite immaterial whether one was German, Danish, or English. I also learnt something perhaps even more important, namely, that in science a decision can always be reached as to what is right and what is wrong. It was not a question of belief, or *Weltanschauung,* or hypothesis; but a certain statement could either be simply right and another statement simply wrong. Neither origin nor race decides the question: it is decided by nature, or if you prefer, by God, in any case not by man.

Summary

In this review of various ways in which both science and Christianity can be viewed as human communities, we have perhaps been able to glimpse something of their profound similarities and deep underlying compatibility. We have also seen something of the many faceted character of community itself. Each of the routes to an understanding of it—as a social structure of interpersonal relationships and dependencies; in terms of a typical biography of a person who passes through it and is formed by it, or in terms of the kind of person it produces; through the image of reality or outlook on life which it provides for those within it; through its history; and in terms of other communities within which it is placed and with which it interacts—each one of these is capable of an extensive development for both science and Christianity of a character which it has been possible to only briefly indicate and suggest here. Yet perhaps the little that has been done has been sufficient to indicate the great fruitfulness of each of these lines of inquiry. Quite clearly substantial gains in the way of deeper and more profound insights into both science and Christianity are to be had in this way.

There remain, of course, crucial problems in the area of content and subject matter which are not touched upon at all in such an approach. There are serious questions about the basis of knowledge in each field, of verification and revelation, of nature and supernature, and many others which a discussion in terms of community simply avoids. Some of these will be dealt with in subsequent chapters. They are valid questions and it is proper that they should be raised and honestly faced. It is my own conviction, however, that there are many hazards and pitfalls in grappling with such questions in terms of subject matter alone. Those who attempt it cannot, of necessity, escape doing so from within whatever community their insights and understandings have been gained. To begin, therefore, by recognizing this simple fact at the outset and concentrating one's attention first on the community seems the better way. For me, in any event, it has been an approach which was almost forced upon me by the peculiarities of my own experience. I have seen many of these problems and questions emerge in an entirely new light with quite unsuspected aspects when, after having seen them for a long time from the vantage point of a physicist, it was given me to view them later from within the Faith. The experience of discovering that the same thing can look quite differently when viewed from a different vantage point naturally turns one's attention to the role of the vantage point. One comes to feel that this is a prior matter which must be dealt with satisfactorily before one can safely proceed. But the vantage point in the case of both science and Christianity is, of course, the community. So it is that I have dealt in these first two chapters with the nature of each as community. Now that that has been done, we are in a position to begin cautiously to deal with some of the problems which emerge out of their respective content.

It is not my intention, however, to attempt in this context a systematic treatment of the interrelationship of the subject matter of science and of Christianity. The primary theme will remain that of community and the way in which knowledge of reality comes through experiences in community. Incidental to my main theme, I will have occasion in the next two chapters to deal with the questions of the reality of spirit and the reality of the supernatural. In either case an exhaustive or systematic treatment is not intended, nor is the treatment meant to suggest that there are not a number of other questions in which scientific and religious categories of thought lead to conflicting evaluations of reality. The specific questions cited have been chosen mainly because of the way in which the idea of community and the question of knowledge enters into their consideration. In the end the problem of knowledge and the role of community in opening up new insights and understanding will be the main theme. Only those issues between science and religion which bear on this theme will be discussed and, even then, only to the extent to which they illuminate the process by which knowledge comes through community.

III

The Reality of Spirit

WHEN ONE asks what is the source of the vitality, power, coherence, and unity of a community, one can find no better explanation than that which the spirit of the community affords. For the soul of any community, whether for good or for evil, is the spirit of the community. And it is this spirit which gives it life and vigor. We say that it is only through community that persons can be made and that personhood is discovered, created, or realized. If we ask, then, by what power the community is able to operate on its members so as to bring out their personhood, we shall doubtless answer by saying that it is the spirit of the community which accomplishes this. At least this will be true of our answers if we are not trying to be scientific about them. Should we seek a scientifically acceptable answer in sociological terms, we would avoid altogether the use of the word "spirit." In that case, however, we would also have to resort to long and complicated answers using several sociologically acceptable terms in order to avoid mentioning "spirit." Moreover, our answer will not be one having the elemental simplicity of the phenomenon we are attempting to interpret and will probably leave us with an uneasy sense of having left out or missed an important element of what we were trying to understand.

During the major portion of the history of mankind the interpretation of man's experience has not been dominated by scientific categories of explanation. From the earliest point at which men in any culture have expressed themselves in a written literature they have used the word "spirit" as a means of communicating to others what would appear to be, on purely empirical grounds, an elemental quality of the common experience of all mankind. Even scientists in their ordinary conversation when they are not being consciously scientific will speak of the "spirit of science" in order to communicate in a simple, direct way something which they have experienced and others can readily respond to out of their own experience. It would appear that the word is likely to continue in common usage in spite of its unacceptability from the standpoint of scientific standards of explanation.

The Meaning of the Word "Spirit"

Human experience, however, is not a static thing and as a consequence the language we employ to communicate it with others is continually changing. Words gradually acquire new meanings and connotations and this must always be kept in mind in the study of literature. There is certainly something universal in the common experience of mankind to which a word such as "spirit" refers. At the same time, however, man's experience of that something has clearly developed, evolved, and slowly changed, and with this development has come a corresponding change in the connotation of the word.

We can see this process in operation in the changing meanings of the contrasting words "spirit" and "matter." In the history of human thought this contrast has always represented some kind of division among the realities man has experienced. In any discussion of science and religion today it still represents a fundamental distinction within the whole of reality which we experience. Yet, at the same time, our understanding of reality has been subject to great changes, particularly during the last few centuries. As a result, although we still make use of this distinction, there is much confusion as to the meaning of the basic terms employed. Just what is meant by "spirit" and by "matter"? The terms are generally taken for granted as though they referred to direct and axiomatic elements in the common experience of all. Yet in the contemporary context this is precisely what one must not do. For in the modern world neither "spirit" nor "matter" refer to any generally agreed-upon elements of experience. We are in a transitional stage in which many of the connotations of former usage have had to be revised or rejected. When the words are used, we are never sure which of the traditional meanings the user may have in mind, or to what extent his revisions and rejections of former understandings correspond to ours.

One of the most widespread features of contemporary thought is the almost universal disbelief in the reality of spirit. Just a few centuries ago the world of spirits was as populous and real as the world of material entities. Not only in popular thought but in that of the highly educated as well was this true. Demons, fairies, angels, and a host of other spiritual beings were as much a part of the experiential world of western man as were rocks and trees and stars. In such a world the words "matter" and "spirit" both referred to directly known realities in the common experience of all. In it important elements of Christianity and of the Biblical view of reality in general, which now cause us much difficulty, could be responded to quite naturally and spontaneously.

The progress of science over these last few centuries and the gradual replacement of Biblical by scientific categories of reality have to a large extent emptied the spirit world of the entities which previously populated it. In carrying out this program science has undoubtedly performed a very considerable service for which it can claim due credit. The objectification of the world of spirit in popular superstition had certainly gone far beyond what the experience of spirit could justify or support. Science is fully competent to deal with any element of experience which arises from an object in space and time. When, therefore, it turned its attention to the concrete entities with which popular imagination had peopled the world of spirit, these entities soon lost whatever status they had enjoyed as actual elements of external reality. In doing so science has unquestionably cleared up widespread misconceptions, removed extraneous and illusory sources of fear, and dispelled many undesirable popular superstitions. There have been, indeed, many important and valuable gains from the development of our present scientific view of the world for which we may be rightly grateful.

All this has not, however, been an unmixed blessing. The scientific debunking of the spirit world has been in a way too successful and too thorough. The house has been swept so clean that contemporary man has been left with no means, or at best with wholly inadequate means, for dealing with his experience of spirit. Although the particular form of conceptualization which popular imagination had made in response to the experience of spirit was undoubtedly defective, the raw experience itself which led to such excesses remains with us as vividly as ever. We simply find ourselves in the position of having no means for inquiring into the structure and meaning of this range of our experience. There is no framework or structure of thought with respect to which we can organize it and no part of reality, as we know and apprehend it, with respect to which we can refer this experience. Science has simply left us helpless and powerless in this important sector of our lives.

The situation in which we find ourselves is brought out with dramatic force in Arthur Miller's play *The Crucible,* which deals with the Salem witch trials. As the play opens the audience is introduced to the community of Salem in Puritan America at the end of the eighteenth century. Aside from a quaint concern with witches and devils which provides the immediate problem in the opening scene, it is a quite normal community. The conversation of the characters creates an atmosphere suggesting the usual mixture of pleasures, foibles, irritations, and concerns which would characterize the common life of a normal village in any age. There is no occasion to feel uneasy or disturbed about these people. Instead, the audience can sit back at ease and, from the perspective of an enlightened time which no longer believes in such things, enjoy the dead seriousness with which the characters in the play take the witches and devils which are under discussion. A teenage girl, Abigail Williams, is being sharply questioned by her minister uncle, the Reverend Samuel Parris, about a wild night affair in the woods in which she and some other girls had seemed to have had contact with these evil beings. For all involved in this discussion the devil is a real entity who can really be confronted in the woods on a dark night, the demon world is populated with real creatures, and witches actually can be seen flying through the air.

As the play unfolds, however, the audience is subtly brought into the grip of an awful evil which grows with ominously gathering power and soon engulfs the community. Everyone in Salem, saint and sinner alike, is swept up by it. It is like a mysterious epidemic which, starting first with Abigail and Parris, spreads inexorably with a dreadfully growing virulence through the whole town until all have been infected by it. It grows terribly and unavoidably in power and leaves in its wake a trail of misery, moral disintegration, and destruction. The audience leaves the play under a spell. It is the kind of spell which the exposure to spirit in its living active manifestation always evokes.

If one asks about this play, what it is that comes upon this community and works within it with such terrible power, there is no better answer to give than "spirit." This is not to attempt to say what spirit is, but only to employ a commonly used word to designate or simply identify a common experience. In the end the good man, John Proctor, expresses what the audience has already come to feel when he says, "A fire, a fire is burning! I hear the boot of Lucifer, I see his filthy face!" The tragic irony of the play is that the very belief in and concern with a devil who could be met in the woods and combatted with formulae set out in books was the very thing that prevented them from detecting the real devil when he came among them. We marvel at their blindness for not seeing this. Yet are not we of the mid-twentieth century, who rightly do not believe there is any such "thing" as the devil, just as bad off as they—only in a different way? In our disbelief we think that we can no longer even use the word and so are unable to even name the elemental power which is so vividly real in this play. We are left helpless to cope with it because we do not dare speak of it as anything real for fear that to do so would imply a commitment to that which has already been discredited and proved false.

Even Mr. Miller himself seems uncertain on this score. In a long commentary which he has inserted in the published text of the first act of the play, he says at one point:

> However, that experience never raised a doubt in his mind as to the reality of the underworld or the existence of Lucifer's many-faced lieutenants. And his belief is not to his discredit. Better minds than Hale's were—and still are—convinced that there is a society of spirits beyond our ken. (page 33)

On the other hand, a little later on he says:

> Since 1692 a great but superficial change has wiped out God's beard and the Devil's horns, but the world is still gripped between two diametrically opposed absolutes. The concept of unity, in which positive and negative are attributes of the same force, in which good and evil are relative, ever-changing, and always joined to the same phenomenon—such a concept is still reserved to the physical sciences and to the few who have grasped the history of ideas. . . . When we see the steady and methodical inculcation into humanity of the idea of man's worthlessness—until redeemed—the necessity of the Devil may become evident as a weapon, a weapon designed and used time and time again in every age to whip men into a surrender to a particular church or church-state. (page 34)

Apparently he does not intend that those who read or view this play should think of the devil as being actually real. Yet such is the dramatic power of his writing that the audience is nevertheless left in the grip of the terrible power and potency of that which came over Salem. It casts a spell upon them so that they leave with a feeling of having been in the mysterious presence of an evil power. It is not enough in accounting for this feeling to analyze it into the wickedness of individual people added together to produce a cumulative effect. For this does not account for the integral, elemental power of that which grows with abounding vigor as the play unfolds, nor does it explain the strange numinous sense of presentness which comes over those who watch the play like a spell. The reality of spirit emerges in this play in spite of the author's convictions to the contrary.

Spirit and Community

There is nothing in the whole range of human experience more widely known and universally felt than spirit. Apart from spirit there could be no community, for it is spirit which draws men into community and gives to any community its unity, cohesiveness, and permanence. Think, for example, of the spirit of the Marine Corps. Surely this is a reality we all acknowledge. We cannot, of course, assign it any substance. It is not material and is not a "thing" occupying space and time. Yet it exists and has an objective reality which can be experienced and known. So it is too with many other spirits which we all know: the spirit of Nazism or Communism, school spirit, the spirit of a street corner gang or a football team, the spirit of Rotary or the Ku Klux Klan. Every community, if it is alive has a spirit, and that spirit is the center of its unity and identity.

In searching for clues which might lead us to a fresh apprehension of the reality of spirit, the close connection between spirit and community is likely to prove the most fruitful. For it is primarily in community that we know and experience spirit. It is spirit which gives life to a community and causes it to cohere. It is the spirit which is the source of a community's drawing power by means of which others are drawn into it from the world outside so that the community grows and prospers. Yet the spirit which lives in community is not identical with the community. The idea of community and the idea of spirit are two distinct and separable ideas.

One characteristic of the spirit in community is its givenness. The members of the community do not create the spirit but rather find it present and waiting for them. It is for them a given which they and they alone possess. The spirit of the Marine Corps was present and operative before any of the present members of it came into it. It is they, of course, who keep it alive and preserve it so the same spirit will continue to be present in the Corps for future recruits to find as they come into it. But if you were to suggest that in doing so they were really creating or generating the spirit in a way which made it originate with them so as to have no reality apart from them, they would vehemently deny it. Rather the spirit of the Marine Corps is something apart from them from which they receive sustenance, power, and life. It is greater than, and distinct from, the whole corporate body of marines. They know that they must ever be vigilant to nourish and sustain it, since otherwise there would be grave danger of its leaving the Corps, or perhaps just dying out. But even then, if such a thing were to happen we all know there would still be a possibility of renewing it or bringing it back if there were a sufficiently poignant sense of loss and ardent desire for its return. In such a case, however, it would definitely not be true that the members of the Corps would feel that they had generated out of themselves a new spirit similar to the former one. It would rather be experienced by all of them as the return of that which had been lost. Every community experiences its own spirit as a gift which it has received from outside itself.

Holy Spirit in the Church

There are close parallels in this and other respects with the Holy Spirit in the Church. In this case the givenness of the Spirit as experienced in the community is made concrete and specific by the historic event of Pentecost. But even apart from this event, the vivid reality of the Holy Spirit as God's gift of himself to the Church has been directly known and experienced by the faithful as the central fact of their communal life in all of the great periods of the Church. Moreover there is always the realization of the possibility of the withdrawal of the gift of the Spirit through the failure of the community to maintain a proper dwelling place for him. The familiar versicle and response, "O God, make clean our hearts within us; And take not thy Holy Spirit from us," gives poignant expression to the fear of such a loss. In the Epistle to the Ephesians in connection with the warning to put away from the communal life all bitterness, wrath, clamor, slander, and malice, we are admonished, "And do not grieve the Holy Spirit of God, in whom you were sealed for the day of redemption" (4:30,31). This same thought is expressed even more fully in that remarkable little book from the same period, *The Shepherd of Hermas,* which came so near to being included in our New Testament. There in his fifth command the shepherd admonishes Hermas:

> If you be patient, the Holy Spirit that dwells in you will be pure. He will not be darkened by any evil spirit, but, dwelling in a broad region, he will rejoice and be glad; and with the vessel in which he dwells he will serve God in gladness, having great peace within himself. But if any outburst of anger take place, forthwith the Holy Spirit, who is tender, is straitened, not having a pure place, and he seeks to depart. For he is choked by the vile spirit and cannot attend on the Lord as he wishes, for anger pollutes him. (Mand. V, 1:2,3; Ante-Nicene Fathers)

No aspect of the Catholic faith is likely to cause more difficulty for people today than the doctrine of the Holy Spirit. The other two Persons of the Holy Trinity have points of reference in even contemporary religious experience by means of which relevant discussion can take place. Even those who have lost the sense of the centrality of the Incarnation still have something to which they can refer the ideas of God the Father and of God the Son. But they are likely to be at a loss when it comes to God the Holy Spirit. However vague they may be in their understanding of the person of Jesus Christ, they at least have such a concrete figure in mind to which they can make reference when God the Son is spoken of. But when one speaks of God the Holy Spirit, no corresponding reality in the experience of the Church comes to mind to which a similar reference can be made.

This difficulty, it seems to me, is the result of the widespread individualization which Christianity has undergone during the last century. Each person is expected to have a private distinctive faith of his own. Much of the contemporary popular religious appeal is directed toward the acquisition of such a faith. The emphases are on such themes as individual conversion, individual religious experience, peace of mind, relief from anxiety, and personal commitment. This individual emphasis has been given striking expression in the popular radio series by Edward R. Murrow, called *This I Believe*. In the great popularity and enthusiastic reception which this series of diverse and largely naïve professions of private faith by prominent figures of our land has enjoyed, we can see disturbing evidence of the religious bankruptcy of our time. Indeed, this widespread conviction that religion is a private, individual, and almost exclusively subjective affair is the most difficult thing I personally have to contend with in responding to the insistent demands which continue to be made upon me to give an account of what impelled me to seek Holy Orders. It is almost in vain that I explain that I have no faith of my own, any more than I have a private physics of my own. People feel that I am somehow begging the question.

The result of this widespread reduction of Christianity to a private, individual experience and faith has been to reduce the Church to the status of little more than an association of like-minded individuals. In part this may be said to be a result of the fragmentation of the Church into many denominations and innumerable sects, which has been one of the most regrettable fruits of the Protestant Reformation. The subjective notion in operation with the objective fragmentation has emptied the idea of the One, Holy, Catholic, and Apostolic Church of Christ of practically all meaning. As a result the great New Testament images of the Church as the Body of Christ, the Bride of Christ, or the branches on the True Vine which is Christ, are largely lost today as symbols of a living reality which we know and share in our own experience.

In this situation it is small wonder that Christians quite generally find difficulty in understanding the doctrine of the Holy Spirit. For the Holy Spirit belongs to that community of the faithful in Christ which is the Holy Catholic Church just as much as the Marine spirit belongs to the Marine Corps. To try to think of the Holy Spirit being given to individual Christians without any such thing as a Catholic Church is just as unintelligible as trying to think of the marine spirit being given to assorted soldiers who call themselves marines without any such thing as a Marine Corps. The Holy Spirit, like other spirits, is corporate rather than individual. Speaking in contemporary scientific terms, we would say that the manifestations of his presence are primarily sociological rather than psychological. The Holy Spirit dwells in community; individuals partake of the power of the Spirit only by virtue of being a part of the community.

Holy Spirit in the New Testament

The widespread tendency to think of Christianity in exclusively individualistic terms has resulted in making the numerous New Testament references to the Spirit abstruse and mystifying to modern readers of Holy Scripture. Especially in the Acts of the Apostles and the Pauline Epistles, readers who are otherwise quite pious and dedicated Christians are likely to find the often passionate references to the Spirit difficult to correlate with anything tangible in their own experience of the Christian life. Yet they will, at the same time, be aware that Saint Luke and Saint Paul are each speaking of something which is obviously a vivid reality in the immediate experience of their hearers. There is never any necessity to explain what is meant by the Spirit. Rather they seem to be able to count at every point on a spontaneous responsiveness from all to whom their words are addressed, as though they referred to a common reality known directly without reflection or intellectual inquiry in the immediate experience of all. This contrast between his own experience of the Holy Spirit and that of the early Church is often a source of considerable bewilderment for the modern Christian.

The key for making a beginning at dispelling this bewilderment is the realization of the corporate reference of the Holy Spirit throughout the New Testament. One practical way to apply this key is to remind oneself wherever the word "you" is employed in the Bible that what is being addressed almost always is the community of the faithful as a corporate body rather than isolated individual Christians. This is a subtle distinction, but at the same time a vital one for a full understanding of Biblical meanings. The difficulty is that the vast majority of contemporary preaching and teaching employs Biblical passages as though they were addressed to each individual hearer. The sermon exhorts each individual hearer to amend, reform, and choose for his or her own benefit without reference to the quality of the community of which they are a part. The text on which it is preached is used as though it were addressed to each individual hearer in isolation from others, whereas the character of the community as a corporate whole is almost always its decisive point. In this way we are all thoroughly conditioned to read into each "you" an individual reference. It requires a conscious effort to recast the passage in our minds so as to make evident its corporate reference. Yet the effort will reward those who make it by opening up the Bible to them in ways which illuminate and make clear many passages which were previously obscure and difficult.

When the author of Ephesians says: "In him you also, who have heard the word of truth, the gospel of your salvation, and have believed in him, were sealed with the promised Holy Spirit" (1:13), the modern reader is likely to think of any individual who, having heard the gospel and being converted, receives in return a mysterious something called the Holy Spirit which comes into him individually. Yet the entire letter is clearly addressed "To the saints who are also faithful in Christ Jesus" as a distinctive corporate body. A careful reading of the passage in its context makes it quite clear that it is not referring to a sequence of isolated individual conversions, but to that which already characterizes all the members of a particular kind of community, the Church. It is this community, this corporate whole, which has been sealed with the promised Holy Spirit. Indeed it was to this community, not to isolated Christians, that the Lord promised to send the Paraclete; and it was upon this community, with all of its members assembled in patient expectation, that the Holy Spirit descended on Pentecost. Ever after, individual members of the community have been enabled to participate in the Spirit only by virtue of their membership in the community.

Another approach which has great value in understanding the meaning of the Holy Spirit in the New Testament is to interpret each passage referring to him by means of analogy with a community possessing a vigorous spirit which we all know and recognize, such as the Marine Corps spirit. There are many ways in which this analogy can be employed to clear up otherwise difficult aspects of the doctrine of the Spirit. As a first example of the application of this analogy, let us consider the problem of the unique status of the sin against the Holy Spirit. It has been a source of considerable difficulty to many that our Lord should have singled out this one particular sin as the only one which could not be forgiven. They are puzzled about what could be the special and distinctive features of this particular sin which would set it apart from all other sins in such a dramatic way. With this difficulty in mind, let us consider the analogous situation in the Marine Corps and ask what kinds of misdeeds on the part of one of its members the Corps is able to deal with, and what kinds it is powerless to overcome.

Individual marines do, of course, occasionally behave in ways contrary to the standards of the Corps. As with every other human community, its members fail in various ways and at various times to live up to the ideals and values which constitute the central character of the community. The marines have their own system of discipline to punish, correct, and restore a member who has committed such an act. If we now ask whether among all the things a marine might do, there are certain acts so bad as to lie outside this system, we must acknowledge that in practice there are several for which the only practical recourse is a dishonorable discharge. At first thought we might be tempted to identify these as the "unforgivable sins" in the Marine Corps. On second thought, however, we may find it difficult to single out any one of these as being of such a character as to make it essentially unforgivable, regardless of how important it might be to the Corps to retain and restore a particular marine who had committed it. The degree of discipline, prolonged attention, and effort required of the Corps might not make the result worth it in most cases, but it is difficult to assert that it could *not* be done even if it were worth the effort required.

There is, however, one particular sin which has a quite different status in this respect. This is the sin against the spirit of the marines itself. A marine who has sinned in this way really leaves the Corps powerless to do anything further with him. For to sin against the spirit is simply to deny the spirit. Rather than being attracted to it, longing to share and participate in it, and being lifted and exalted by its power, one comes instead to detest it, to seek only to escape from it, and when even then it is present, to be immune to its power. Whenever this happens the Corps is really helpless to do anything about it. It is powerless to correct and restore such a marine, not because it does not want to, but because it no longer has any resources for dealing with him. This, indeed, is true of every community of whatever character. A member who sins against the spirit of the community has done the one thing which leaves the community powerless to forgive and restore him. In the case of a nation we call it treason. In the case of the Church it is the sin against the Holy Spirit. If, however, we make Christianity over into an individualistic private affair so that there is nothing left of the Church in its catholic sense, in which the Holy Spirit can dwell, then, of course, the unique status of the sin against the Holy Spirit does come to seem arbitrary, unreasonable, and rigidly doctrinaire.

Another aspect of the doctrine of the Holy Spirit which this analogy is helpful in illuminating is the assertion that the Holy Spirit is available only through the Church to its members. In spite of the clear Biblical foundation of this doctrine, it is frequently a source of difficulty for contemporary Protestant Christians. Why, they ask, should God withhold his Holy Spirit from one who follows the teachings of Jesus as he finds them set forth in his Bible simply because he has not joined some church? Such people are strongly individualistic in their Christianity and often in opposition to organized religion. They feel that they should have just as much claim on God's concern and the gifts of his grace as the members of any church or sect. To limit the gift of the Holy Spirit to those who have been made members of Christ in his Church, as the New Testament unquestionably does, seems to them an arbitrary and unjustified exclusiveness. This point of view, however, is the result of a failure to appreciate the corporate character of the indwelling of the Holy Spirit, as can be made quite clear by means of our analogy.

Let us consider the same question in terms of the conditions under which one can possess the Marine spirit. Here it is quite evident that the only way for a young man to have the Marine Corps spirit for himself is to actually become a full member of the Marine Corps. He must start from the beginning, go through boot camp, subject himself to the authority and discipline involved, until finally the day arrives when he is taken in as a full-fledged marine. Then, and then only, can he have for himself the spirit of the Marine Corps. Moreover, when that time comes the spirit is simply given to him without effort or striving on his part. It simply comes to him as an integral part of the process of his incorporation into the Corps. Clearly by the very nature of the case only marines can have the Marine spirit. All the rest of us must of necessity merely observe it from the outside without possessing it for ourselves. In recognizing and accepting this simple fact, we do not, however, rebel against it as though it were an arbitrary requirement unjustly imposed upon us. It is obviously not a question of justice or rules at all, but something essential to the nature of the Marine spirit itself.

In the New Testament, as well as in the practice and experience of the Church throughout the major portion of its subsequent history, something similar may be said about the work of the Holy Spirit in the Church. Those received into the Church by Baptism and Confirmation already have the Holy Spirit without doing anything more about it, just as much as those who become members of the Marine Corps already possess its spirit without doing anything more about it. Those outside, in either case, simply cannot possess that of which they are not a part. This is not a matter of injustice or arbitrary legislation, but a simple consequence of the nature of things. Of course, in an age in which the Church has lost much of its sense of corporateness, none of its members will experience his possession of the Spirit with anything like the vividness with which the Marine spirit is experienced. In that case, however, it is no solution to try to reinterpret the Holy Spirit as an individual gift independent of the Church. All one can do is wait patiently in earnest and expectant prayer for his return in power to the corporate body to which he belongs.

The Corporate Nature of Spirit

In placing so much emphasis on the corporate nature of spirit, there is danger of falling into a too easy generalization. Thus one might suppose that the possession of the spirit would be confined to those moments when the corporate body was actually physically assembled. But if we consider this question in the light of our Marine analogy, we shall see that this is not the case. Think, for example, of a marine who has been assigned to duty on some remote one-man post, an island or a mountain-top lookout perhaps, for an extended period. He serves by himself without seeing another marine for a long time. If now we ask whether a marine on such a duty assignment would thereby lose possession of the Marine spirit, the answer is clearly negative. He will instead in his solitude do many things to keep alive in himself the spirit of the Marine Corps. At night he will sing marine songs to the stars, during the day he will often recall to mind past incidents of his life in the Corps, and at all times he will derive strength for his task from the sense of profound fellowship which he knows he continues to enjoy with his fellow marines. It is, of course, the same with the Holy Spirit in the Church. One can be a lone missionary in a foreign land or an anchorite hermit in the desert and continue to possess the Holy Spirit. In doing so, however, one does not in any sense cease to be a member of that holy fellowship in the Lord, the Church, or abandon the sense of belonging within the intimacy of the household of God which life in the Church provides for all of its members. The indwelling of the Holy Spirit in the Body of Christ is a much more profound and subtle thing than any merely transient phenomenon associated with a physical association of persons in actual fellowship, although it is, of course, most manifest and evident when the whole community is actually gathered together as a corporate whole.

One ought not suppose either that the reality of the spirit in community is dependent on the complete sharing in it of all of the members of the community. One can conceive of the possibility, far in the future, of the Marine Corps sinking to such depths that the great majority of its members would serve in it purely as mercenaries with no loyalty and no spirit. In such an eventuality it might still happen, however, that a small and scattered band of marines would still remain who were on fire with the true spirit of the Corps and who would suffer in agony over the low estate to which the Corps had fallen. This is indeed, in the case of Israel, the idea of the Remnant which is encountered so frequently in the Prophets and elsewhere in the Bible and which at times has been experienced in the Church. Again the idea of the spirit in community is much more subtle and substantial than would be the case if it were merely a quality or property which would have to be manifested by a major portion of its membership, or which could be annihilated at will by the action of a sufficient number of members having a formal association with it.

There may be those who will raise an objection to the use of an analogy such as that of the Marine Corps in order to interpret the doctrine of the Holy Spirit, on the basis that the latter is unique, being in fact none other than God himself, the third person of the Holy Trinity, whereas the former is a merely human aspect of an entirely non-religious, man-made association. It is true, of course, that there are a vast number and variety of spirits in community and that they range all the way from the most demonic to the most divine. It is also true that among this whole diverse spectrum of spirits, the Holy Spirit occupies a unique and completely exalted position. Neither of these assertions, however, destroys the usefulness or the propriety of the analogy which we have employed. This can best be seen by comparing this situation with that which is already familiar to us in the case of the second Person of the Trinity. In one very valid sense it is of course true to say of our Lord Jesus Christ that he is uniquely set apart from all other members of the human species by virtue of being the Incarnate Son of God, a claim which cannot be made for any other human person who has ever lived. But we would stand convicted of heresy if we left the matter there without emphasizing, at the same time, that he was nevertheless very man of very man, fully human in every respect, except for sin, as we are human, and therefore fully comparable to every other member of the human species in his humanity—even to the extent of including the most corrupt and wicked individuals which that species has produced.

The relationship of the Holy Spirit to other spirits is quite analogous to this. The process by which we bring to mind every member of the species *Homo sapiens* who has inhabited this planet and from all of them single out one individual, Jesus Christ, and assert of him that he was none other than the Incarnate Son of God is essentially the same as that by which we bring to mind every human community which has ever been formed in all history and single out one only of all of them, the Holy Catholic Church, and assert of it that the Spirit which dwells within it and empowers it is, in distinction to the spirits which dwell in all other communities, none other than God, the Holy Spirit himself. Both of these are astounding assertions which throughout the whole history of Christian evangelism have often seemed completely incredible, sheer foolishness, or a stumbling block. But they constitute together, nevertheless, the Gospel, the good news of God in Jesus Christ, which it is the central mission of the Church to proclaim. To claim, therefore, that it is wrong to say that the Holy Spirit in the Church is analogous to the spirit of the Marine Corps would be like saying that it is wrong to compare Jesus in his humanity to an individual marine.

Every spirit, by the very nature of the operation of spirit in community itself, has a power over human lives and a capacity to mold and transform human persons which is similar to the power of the Holy Spirit in the Church to seize, transform, redeem, and save. Consider, for example, some of the exceedingly powerful spirits which have scourged humanity in the last few decades: the spirits of Italian Fascism, German Nazism, and Marxist Communism. The terrible fascination which these demonic communities have for many persons and their consequent capacity to grow powerfully has been noted by all of us. Once incorporated into such a community, the experience of the individual is often strikingly similar to that of religious conversion. Communist literature from Russia, Poland, China and elsewhere today gives many moving testimonials to this fact. Those who really believe in Communism with their whole heart have a faith in it and a loyalty and devotion to it so total and complete as to be baffling to many free world readers. There is a sense of the unquenchable power and certain victory of the spirit and movement which they serve, which is remarkably parallel to that found in Saint Luke's Acts of the Apostles. The individual feels himself lifted, empowered, and redeemed by the spirit of the Party in a way entirely similar to the corresponding experience in the Church. There is the same sense of newness of life, of having been rescued from bondage to a worthless and perishing self, of enjoying for the first time a sense of the grandness of freedom in the service of that which is great and noble and true—a genuine experience, in other words, of real redemption and personal salvation. Fascism and Nazism produced essentially the same effect on those who were captivated by them, especially on the youth of the interwar period.

Spirit and Holy Spirit

There is nothing more terrible than the agony of soul of one who, having given himself totally and without reservation to such a movement, is forced slowly to the dawning realization that the spirit which has given him so much and acquired such power over him is in actuality demonic and not at all the divine power he so confidently believed it to be when he first gave himself over to it. Moving testimonies to this agony have been given in a book, edited by Richard Crossmann and published under the title, *The God That Failed*, in which a number of former communists give an account of their experiences in Communism and of the reasons for their breaking away from it. A similar testimonial in great detail is given in Whittaker Chambers' book *The Witness*. What is brought home with great force in accounts such as these is the terrible reality and power of spirit in community both to give life and, when it is demonic, to destroy. Moreover, it also is very clear from these accounts that the demonic is never recognized as such at the outset. The spirit which attracts and draws into community always seems good, noble, and divine. It is only much later and well after the power of the spirit to give life, even in abundance, has been known and experienced, that the discovery of its demonic character slowly, fearfully, and reluctantly dawns upon the, by then, almost helpless victim. What everyone in these dark days has come to recognize as a crucial need is for some way to test the spirits in advance of committing oneself to one of them. To stand back from every association into community for fear of the power of a demonic spirit to destroy is not a feasible alternative. A completely autonomous self is a lone and isolated island of mortal and finite being in the midst of an infinite, cold, and alien universe. Only the spirit, whether for weal or woe, can give life. Without it the self can only shrivel up, perish, and die eternally.

This problem of selecting that particular community whose spirit only operates to give life and fulfill the personhood of all in its service is the central and fundamental problem of the Bible. In Biblical terms it is the problem of idolatry, of avoiding the worship and service of all false gods, and choosing the one true God so as to follow him only. As Elijah put it to the people gathered before him on Mount Carmel, "How long will you go limping with two different opinions? If Yahweh is God, follow him; but if Baal, then follow him" (I Kings 18:21). Indeed, in a world in which there is no man-made criterion for testing one god or one spirit against another, it was always the special claim and witness of Israel that to her, and to her alone, the one true God had revealed himself. It is this which has made her a scandal among all other nations and peoples, and at the same time has defined her special destiny "to be a light to lighten the Gentiles."

The New Testament carries on and amplifies the same theme. It does so against the background of a keen and lively appreciation of the power of the demonic spirit to capture human lives and destroy them. It does so through the rich and expressive imagery of the age in which it was written. Many of those who came to our Lord in his incarnate life for healing were recognized by him as victims of the power of the demonic over them. Throughout his ministry he evidenced a deep sensitivity to the power of spirit over men and the terrible need in which all men stand to be rescued from this dreadful power through the gift of the One Spirit, with ultimate power to triumph over all others, which gives life and freedom to eternity without ever destroying. In the New Testament world the spirits of such fearful power which we recognize in our time under the names of Fascism, Nazism, and Communism go under the names of principalities, dominions, and powers; but other than nomenclature there is no essential difference between them. Those who by the grace and mercy of God have been brought into the fellowship of Christ's Church and now share in the power of the Holy Spirit, can look back on their former estate as one in which they had been "slaves to the elemental spirits of the universe" (Gal. 4:3, Col. 2:8 and 2:20). The author of Ephesians can address them as those whom God, the Holy Spirit, had "made alive, when you were dead through the trespasses and sins in which you once walked, following the course of this world, following the prince of the power of the air, the spirit that is now at work among the sons of disobedience. Among these we all once lived in the passions of our flesh, following the desires of body and mind, and so we were by nature children of wrath like the rest of mankind" (2:1-3).

It is against this background that the great central drama to which the Christian faith bears witness took place. Into a world caught up in the grip of demonic spirits bent on destruction, the Son of God "for us men and for our salvation came down from heaven . . . and was made man." To those who had in vain desperately sought a spirit in community to which they could give themselves to salvation rather than destruction, the Good News could now be proclaimed that "God so loved the world that he gave his only begotten Son, to the end that all who believe in him should not perish, but have everlasting life." Through those who had now been sealed with the promised Holy Spirit within that holy fellowship, the Church, "the plan of the mystery hidden for ages in God who created all things" was now made known even to "the principalities and powers in the heavenly places" (Eph. 3:9,10). Hereafter, nothing whatever, no principalities, nor powers, nor any kind of spirit however powerful, "will be able to separate us from the love of God in Christ Jesus our Lord" (Rom. 8:38,39). This victory of cosmic proportions which God in Christ won for man in the world is the core of the Good News, the central proclamation of the Gospel. The culmination of the drama of the Incarnation is Pentecost in which a spirit is given which is none other than God, the Holy Spirit himself, to a community, the Church, which is none other than the Body of

Christ; to the end that even nineteen centuries later when the world would again be swept by dark and terrible spirits, there would still be alive within it that same holy community into which men might be drawn to receive from its Spirit life and joy and fulfillment in abundance.

There is one sure and simple way to test any spirit to which one might be drawn, and have the desire to give oneself to the community which it empowers. This test has been stated clearly and unambiguously by Saint John. "Beloved, do not believe every spirit," he says, "but test the spirits to see whether they are of God. . . . By this you know the spirit of God: every spirit which confesses that Jesus Christ has come in the flesh is of God, and every spirit which does not confess Jesus is not of God" (I St. John 4:1-3). To much of our world today, as it was to Saint John's world then, such a test seems sheer nonsense. What the world demands in such a test in order that it be acceptable is something much more erudite and scientifically respectable than this. Yet science is quite impotent when it comes to the world of spirit, and a test in scientific terms which would be capable of offering real assurance that any given spirit would not ultimately turn its power to the destruction of those who have given themselves to it is not even possible to imagine. When it comes to testing the spirits, St. John's direct and simple test remains, after nineteen centuries of experience with many other more sophisticated formulas, the safest and most reliable we are ever likely to be given. Even the Church, however, as we know from its long history, is susceptible to invasion by the demonic. But it is also true at the same time that the Church, in common with other human associations which acknowledge Jesus Christ as Lord and Saviour, are the only communities known which consistently possess the power within themselves to drive out the demonic, and to emerge, time and again, renewed and restored with the Holy Spirit returned victoriously to dwell again within it.

One of the most powerful cases for the reality of spirit I know of has been made in a book which is at the same time the most passionate and thorough-going rejection of spirit, and of the life in community which it entails, which has ever been written. The book is *The True Believer* by Eric Hoffer. In this book every communal human association of any power, every spirit which energizes such a community, all the way from the Ku Klux Klan to Christianity, is equally to be resisted, feared, and dreaded. All communities are no more than mass movements, and all the spirits which empower them are basically the same and equally dangerous. For Hoffer the only safe course for the individual is a completely autonomous existence, free from every tie which binds into community, unfettered by any believing, and insulated from the power of every spirit. Such a brief summary cannot do justice to this book, and those who find such a bald statement of its central thesis shocking should read the book to see for themselves how convincing and impressive a case can be made for it. It is only the vantage point from which the book is written that is wrong. Apart from this vantage point, it offers a profound understanding and exceptionally clear insights into the nature of the spirit in community, as well as of its power both to create and to destroy persons. By means of it we can be led to see the Spirit in the Church as exactly the same kind of reality as the innumerable spirits which empower all other communities, just as we are accustomed to seeing Jesus as like us in all respects.

To parallel the question asked of St. Peter by Christ, one could ask of the Spirit which resides in the Church, "Who do men say that he is?" To such a question Hoffer would unhesitatingly answer, "Just the same as the spirits which energize all other mass movements." This, we must realize, is from his standpoint a perfectly possible and even reasonable answer. St. Peter's reply to Christ's question was a confession, not an answer which comes as a solution in a process of reasoning. So too we, who would answer this question contrary to Hoffer, "He is none other than the Holy Spirit, the living God himself," must realize that we too are confessing, not solving. The recognition of the uniqueness of Christ as the incarnate Son of God among all other human beings who have ever lived, and the recognition of the uniqueness of the Holy Spirit as the third person of the Holy Trinity among all other spirits in community are acts of the same character. We cannot really reply to a thesis like Hoffer's until we realize that what is involved is a matter of confession and witness, rather than demonstration or reasoned conclusion, in exactly the same way as we understand St. Peter's reply to the same question about our Lord. It is only in this way, I am convinced, that St. John's "test of the spirits" can emerge again in our time and context with the deep meaning and profound relevance to our situation which it surely possesses.

Summary

Our purpose in this chapter has been to deal with the question of the reality of spirit. Let us now see how we have accomplished our objective. The traditional approach in philosophy to this question is to establish reality in terms of substance. The reality of the world of matter rested in the existence of material substance, and in the same way the reality of the world of spirit must be looked for in the existence of spiritual substance. It is natural for us to employ the notion of substance in thinking about the reality of anything which exists outside our own minds. In the context of modern thought, however, we find ourselves immediately in the gravest difficulties whenever the idea of a spiritual substance is introduced. Any of the words available to us for a discussion in such terms are so laden with connotations and meanings from their traditional usage as to make them unacceptable for our purpose. This difficulty is not, however, confined to the idea of spiritual substance alone. We find ourselves in much the same difficulty when we attempt to understand the reality of matter in terms of its essence or underlying substance. As we shall see more fully in the next chapter, modern physics has pushed its investigations into the elementary constituents of matter almost to the limit of the intuitive capacity of the human mind to understand in terms meaningfully derived from direct human experience. In the view of the basic structure of physical reality which physics now holds, the old ideas of the essence of matter and of material substance as the ground of physical reality are just as unacceptable as those related to spiritual reality. We are in a stage of our pilgrimage of understanding when any attempt to deal with the realities of either spirit or matter in philosophical or metaphysical terms seems to involve us in hopeless semantic difficulties.

In these circumstances my own approach to the problem of the reality of spirit has been much the same as that which I would take as a physicist in dealing with the reality of matter. In either case the best one can do under present limitations is to present the whole range of the direct experience of either spirit or matter with the hope that out of such a unified presentation a grasp of the reality of that which is being described will be simply evident. This is all that I have attempted to do in this lecture. My hope has been that the fact of spirit, as a reality of raw human experience, would simply emerge from such a panoramic presentation of the diverse ways in which it confronts us all in much the same way that the reality of matter simply emerges in physics from a systematic presentation of the way in which elementary particles, nuclei, atoms, molecules, etc., are actually observed. Indeed, against the background of the total fact of spirit as a universal element of human experience as it has been presented here, the only way in which it could be pronounced unreal, or dissolved into a mere figment of the imagination, would be on the basis of some *a priori* metaphysical commitment or of some prior theory of knowledge which would automatically exclude this kind of human experience from any contact with reality. This, however, would be to do negatively the same thing which I have explicitly refused to do positively in this presentation.

In defending in this way my adoption of a purely experiential basis for accepting spirit as real, I do not mean to imply, as some do, that metaphysical considerations are meaningless or that the attempt to understand any aspect of reality in terms of its essence must be rejected. On the contrary, I am myself convinced that the metaphysical questions are, in the human quest for understanding and knowledge, the fundamental ones, and that the whole contemporary effort in philosophy to discredit and reject them is doomed to failure simply because they are bound to continue to goad each new generation so insistently and intolerably that men inevitably will be forced by this pressure to develop the necessary semantic apparatus for dealing with them meaningfully. It is simply my own conviction that this process cannot be hurried, however much we may wish to force it to a premature maturity, and that all we can do in our present situation is to acknowledge that we do not yet possess such an apparatus. Such an acknowledgment then leaves us with the kind of presentation of the reality of spirit which has been given here, as a sort of interim measure which represents the only course open to us in the present stage of our understanding.

IV

Nature and Supernature

CLOSELY ALLIED to the question of the reality of spirit are the questions of the reality of the beautiful and of the holy. In this chapter we shall be concerned with the whole category of experience designated by the word "holy," and with the related questions of nature and supernature, and of the existence of a reality transcendent to nature. Our discussion on spirit has, doubtless, already raised these questions, since the idea of spirit is closely related to the idea of the holy as well as to the transcendent and the supernatural. That discussion was, however, almost entirely confined to spirit as experienced in community. When approached in that way, the subject of spirit does not specifically give rise to these related questions because neither the experience of the holy nor the idea of the transcendent arises directly or in any essential way out of life in community. Thus, in contrast to the last chapter, our concern here may be described as having to do with those aspects of spirit which are not directly related to its manifestation in community.

My thinking along these lines first became explicit when I had the experience of reading Rudolf Otto's *Das Heilige*, which is available in an excellent English translation under the title, *The*

Idea of the Holy. It is, I believe, fair to say that Otto's venture in this book represents a new departure in western thought. Nothing quite comparable to it had been attempted before. For me the reading of this book was a liberating experience. It opened to me for the first time the possibility of dealing with a whole range of experience, which is inaccessible to scientific investigation, by methods which are nevertheless entirely agreeable to one trained in a scientific approach to a problem. In order to see the book in this light, it is necessary to go considerably beyond the particular subject of the category of the holy which is its special concern, and to view Otto's achievement from the standpoint of the possibility of a division of all human experience into conceptual and non-conceptual elements. In terms of such a distinction one can say that science is by its nature exclusively concerned only with that portion of experience which can be conceptualized, whereas Otto shows how it is possible to deal meaningfully and fruitfully with a non-conceptual element of experience.

In order to more fully appreciate the implications of this distinction, we need to see the problem with which it deals in the context of the general problem of reality and of the possibility of human knowledge of it. It is not too much to say that the problem of the relationship between the external world and our knowledge of it through perception has been the central concern of philosophy in the West during the last several centuries. This concern has led to a division of all human experience into categories of the objective and the subjective. The human perceiving subject is regarded as standing in some definite relationship to the world about him, the nature of which determines the character of his perceptual experience of it. The specification of the nature of this relationship is the problem of epistemology. The problem divides itself into two parts. The first part consists in the attempt to trace in detail every step in the process by which, starting with the raw data of sense perception—the direct sensations of seeing, hearing, feeling, etc.—at the boundary between the perceiving subject and his external world, an integrated system of knowledge of that world, including even the most sophisticated and abstract scientific theory, is constructed. The second part of the epistemological problem seeks ways in which we can reassure ourselves that our knowledge of the world truly reflects or mirrors what the world apart from our perception of it actually is like.

These two aspects of the problem of knowledge will be the central concern of the next chapter, and we shall go into them in some detail there. For the present purpose we need only concern ourselves with one aspect of the first part of the problem, namely, the conceptualization of experience. Out of the stream of moment-by-moment perceptual experience which passes through his consciousness, the human perceiver extracts elements which he is able to relate to certain mental constructions, called "concepts," which he has formed in his mind. Everyone has a considerable store of concepts in his mind—such as table, sidewalk, rock, tree, star, electron, etc.—which he uses to tie in with his direct perception of the world. As time goes on he finds that he is able to develop more and more complex interrelationships among his store of concepts by means of propositions such as "x implies y," "a is a consequence of b," "p is caused by q," and the like. In this way he is able to organize and correlate his experience into an integrated system of knowledge of the world about him. He hopes and believes that this knowledge he has in his mind is a real and valid reflection of the way the world actually is in itself. That is, he desires that each of the concepts in his mind should correspond with something real which exists in the world outside, and that these outside entities be actually related to each other in the same way that he has rationally related the corresponding concepts in his mind to each other. The chief means by which he reassures himself on this score is by continually referring his store of concepts and the relationships he has established between them back to new perceptual experience. This is what is called in science the process of empirical or experimental verification. An image of reality in one's mind, if it is valid, will behave in the same way that the external world behaves. As a test of this one can use one's knowledge of the world to predict what ought to be observed in a given situation, and then test to see whether one's actual perceptual experience in that situation confirms one's expectations.

This process of testing one's knowledge of the world against one's actual experience of the world is a necessary procedure for everyone, and it would be both wrong and futile to take exception to it. What is commonly done in modern thought, however, goes considerably beyond the well-defined objective of the process and makes it over into a criterion for deciding what portion of one's experience corresponds to external reality and what portion is to be regarded as purely subjective. This criterion is rarely explicitly formulated or recognized, and generally is applied on purely pragmatic or practical grounds. The effect of it, however, is to regard only that portion of experience which meets the test of empirical validation as possessing objective validity independent of the wishes or feelings of the observer, and as constituting, therefore, the only portion of experience which corresponds to external reality. All the rest of experience is assumed to originate wholly within the inner workings of the observer's own mind and to bear no correspondence with anything external to him whose existence would not vanish if he were to vanish.

It is with respect to this widely made, but generally unrecognized, assumption about one's experience that Otto's achievement in his study of the holy has such major importance. The basic question which his study raises is this: Is it not possible that at least some of the elements of our experience out of which we are unable to derive any definable concepts originate, nevertheless, from objective external entities just as real as those related to its conceptual elements? Or, to put the same question in another way, why should one suppose that the structure of his brain and sense organs should be so perfectly matched to a universe—which otherwise is entirely independent of him—that everything which exists in that universe must be capable of conceptual representation in his mind, and, contrariwise, that nothing which his mind is unable to conceive could possibly have any external existence in the universe? Again in terms of the process which we have just described, how can we be sure that, in sifting out of the totality of our experience those elements for which we have definable concepts, we are sifting out completely *only* those elements which correspond to realities external to ourselves? Is all reality necessarily of such a character that it can be conceived by the human mind in the form of concepts which can be related to each other in propositions?

These questions raise the possibility that there may be non-conceptual elements of our experience which correspond to an external reality just as real and just as independent of us as that which corresponds to the conceptual elements of our experience. This possibility suggests that the totality of our experience might be compared to a plum pudding in which the currants or raisins would represent that portion capable of conceptualization, and the rest of the pudding its non-conceptual component. The usual assumption of most contemporary philosophy is the entirely arbitrary requirement that everything which exists in the universe apart from human beings must be mirrored in the currants, while all the rest of the pudding corresponds only to inner states of the human observer, arising, therefore, out of nothing more significant than certain peculiarities of his physiological processes and the structure of his nervous system. Against this background Otto's great achievement consists in making manifest and clearly setting forth, in what may properly be called a strictly scientific manner, a definite and recognizable area of human experience of an essentially non-conceptual character which stands in the same relationship to external reality as does the conceptual portion of our experience. In terms of our analogy, what he does is to point out to us one small part of the pudding and proceed to demonstrate that it quite obviously has the same relationship to external reality as do the currants.

The Idea of the Holy

All this is by way of introduction and setting for a discussion of Otto's book. Nowhere in it does he himself claim for his investigation any such broad or fundamental objective. In carrying out his study, he was not by intention attempting to make a new contribution to western philosophy or to present a new viewpoint on the general epistemological problem with which that philosophy has so largely been concerned. It is, properly speaking, only my interpretation of his book which gives it this much wider application, and I must assume full responsibility for placing his ideas in such an enlarged setting in my discussion of them. All that Otto himself was trying to do, as I interpret his task, was to study and understand as fully as possible that particular category of experience which is designated by the word "holiness" or "the holy." His first step, in conformance with accepted scientific methodology, was to identify and extract the conceptual elements of his subject. As he gives the account of the course of his investigation, this he did at the outset as thoroughly as possible. And he did find, indeed, that, to a greater or lesser extent in the usage of different cultures and at different times and stages in each, a rational element of the experience of the holy could be isolated and identified; and it was expressible in terms of moral and ethical concepts. But the more distinctly he was able to identify and define this conceptual content of the idea of the holy, the more evident it became to him that the most essential and important aspects of the holy involve a clear overplus of meaning which completely eludes apprehension in terms of definable concepts. At this stage the majority of investigators would doubtless have relegated this overplus to the realm of the subjective and abandoned the whole study. Otto, however, to whom the idea of the holy was already something very real, decided instead to turn his attention to the question: whether, after all, it might not prove possible to discover ways of describing and understanding this non-conceptual portion of the total content of the holy.

As in any venture into new and untried territory, the first thing one must do is to define one's terms in order to be able to communicate to others the novel ideas which are involved. The first and most important term which he needed was one which would clearly separate from the word "holy" all of its conceptual content, such as the good and the moral, and designate only the purely non-conceptual overplus which it was his purpose to elucidate. This he did by coining the word "*numinous*" to represent the non-conceptual part of the experience of the holy. This extremely apt word, which has come into common usage as a permanent addition to the language in the forty years since he invented it, he derived from the Latin word *numen* (divinity) in the same way that "ominous" is derived from the Latin *omen*. A numinous experience of the holy is by definition ineffable and inexpressible since it can lead to nothing which the mind is capable of rationally defining or conceptualizing. In terms of the analogy previously employed, if the totality of the experience of the holy is represented by a plum pudding, the currants are the conceptual part of it (good, moral, etc.) while the rest of the pudding in which they are imbedded is the numinous experience.

The next problem with which Otto has to deal appears at first sight to present an insuperable difficulty. Considering that the objective is to present and clearly exhibit elements of experience which cannot be conceptualized and for which, therefore, no verbal or other symbols can be devised, how is it possible to speak or to write about such elements at all? Will not every single word used in the discussion necessarily be the symbol for some concept? And is not every sentence employing these words a representation in propositional form of rational relationships among the concepts which they denote? Certainly every word employed in such a discussion will possess a dictionary definition, the purpose of which is to describe as clearly as possible its conceptual content. Considerations such as these would seem to suggest that a treatise in written language devoted to the exposition of non-conceptual and non-rational elements of experience would be a contradiction in terms.

The resolution of this apparent dilemma lies in the dual role and function of words. In the questions above we are thinking of words in their function of *conveying* concepts to others with whom we wish to communicate. But words are equally well employed for the purpose of *evoking* in others non-conceptual experiences which we wish to share with them. The former function is exemplified by the scientific use of the words "gram," "acceleration," "electron," or "valence"; while the latter function is exemplified by the poetic use of such words as "grisly," "grue," "weird," or "wan." All real language employs words in this double capacity so that they simultaneously convey and evoke. And so we can indeed employ language for the exhibition of non-conceptual experience as, of course, every poet already knows. Otto himself describes the process of evoking such experience in his readers as follows:

> There is only one way to help another to an understanding of it (the numinous). He must be guided and led on by consideration and discussion of the matter through the ways of his own mind, until he reaches the point at which 'the numinous' in him perforce begins to stir, to start into life and into consciousness. We can cooperate in this process by bringing before his notice all that can be found in other regions of the mind already known and familiar, to resemble, or again to afford some special contrast to, the particular experience we wish to elucidate. Then we must add: 'This *x* of ours is not precisely *this* experience, but akin to this one and the opposite of that other. Cannot you now realize for yourself what it is?' In other words our *x* cannot, strictly speaking be taught, it can only be evoked, awakened in the mind; as everything that comes 'of the spirit' must be awakened. (page 7)

After having dealt with these preliminaries, we are now in a position to take up with Otto's assistance the crucial question of the reality of the holy. This involves the question: to what, if anything, in the world external to our experiencing selves, is the experience of the numinous a response? The simplest and easiest answer to this question in the context of our present-day, largely conceptualized, approach to the holy, and to religion in general, would be to say simply that when one experiences the holy one is experiencing the presence of God. But such an answer is, in a way, too sophisticated for Otto's purpose. For if we are to comprehend in our treatment of this subject the whole range of human experience of the holy, from that in the most primitive culture to that in the most advanced, it will be necessary to recognize that in many instances man's actual experience of the holy is as often demonic as it is divine. In order to do justice to this empirical fact, what we need, therefore, is a completely non-committal word to designate the object of a numinous experience. For this purpose Otto invents the equally apt phrase, *mysterium tremendum*, to designate the external object of a numinous experience in the same sense that in the experience of hearing, a vibrating body is the object. The *mysterium tremendum* always implies a something which is intimately, although ineffably, present in a mysterious way. It is that which is often felt in the atmosphere clinging to old churches, lofty cathedrals, haunted houses, sacred shrines or monuments, or traditionally weird and eerie places. It is frequently experienced as peculiarly present on a mountain top, at sea, or in the midst of a storm. Our apprehension of the *mysterium tremendum* comes to us always through a non-conceptual, numinous experience; and this experience has certain definable and recognizable characteristics which are related to corresponding attributes of its object. It is perhaps the outstanding achievement of Otto's book that he has been able to go so far toward specifically identifying these attributes and demonstrating the possibility for a perfectly definite methodology for dealing with them.

In identifying these attributes Otto finds it useful to consider each of the two words used to designate the object of a numinous experience separately. Thus he is led to the assignment of three primary attributes to the *numinous tremendum* and of two to the *numinous mysterium*. We shall review briefly these five characteristics in that order.

The first characteristic of the *numinous tremendum* is the element of *awfulness*. Awe is an essential element in any genuine experience of the holy. When Jacob awoke from his dream at the sanctuary of Bethel, "he was afraid, and said, 'How awesome is this place! This is none other than the house of God.'" (Gen. 28:17) Numinous fear is quite different from the conceptual fear inspired by ordinary created things. There is something spectral about it, an inner dread and shuddering. It is the kind of fear which makes one's "flesh creep" as opposed to the kind which makes one's blood run cold." It can be demonic in character, and often is in primitive religious experience. The poetry of Edgar Allan Poe is an excellent example of the use of words for evoking numinous awe and fear. On its positive side it is the awe inspired by the presence of that which is sacred, hallowed, sanctified. There is a numinous quality about the Biblical usage of "the fear of God" which escapes every effort at rational, conceptual definition.

The second primary element is that of *overpoweringness.* This is the element which is evoked by the sense of the awful majesty of the mysterium tremendum, the sense of the littleness of every creature in the face of that which is above all creatures. Job's concluding words express this element powerfully, "I had heard of thee by the hearing of the ear, but now my eye sees thee; therefore I despise myself, and repent in dust and ashes." (Job 42:5-6) When Isaiah beheld the Lord in the temple, high and lifted up, his response expresses the overpowering character of the experience: "Woe is me! For I am lost; for I am a man of unclean lips, and I dwell in the midst of a people of unclean lips; for my eyes have seen the King, the Lord of hosts!" (Is. 6:5)

The third quality of the numinous tremendum is its *urgency* or *energy.* It is this element which distinguishes the "living" God from the purely "philosophic" God. It presents itself to the feelings with attributes of vitality, passion, emotional temper, will, force, movement, excitement, activity, and impetus. It is this numinous quality which is evoked in the Biblical usage of "the wrath of God" as when the anger of Yahweh flamed forth against Uzzah, or when the author of Hebrews says, "For the word of God is living and active, sharper than any two-edged sword, piercing to the division of soul and spirit, of joints and marrow," or "It is a fearful thing to fall into the hands of the living God," or again "let us offer to God acceptable worship with reverence and awe; for our God is a consuming fire." (Heb. 4:12, 10:31, 12:29)

The first of the primary qualities of the *numinous mysterium* which Otto identifies is that of its being *Wholly Other.* This quality is often expressed negatively as in the "nothingness," "void," or "emptiness" of the mystics, or the strange "Nirvana" of Buddhism with its mysteriously positive quality. It is often symbolized by vast empty reaches of sky or sea which, nevertheless, may seem alive with the complete otherness of numinous being. On its positive side this quality is represented by the words "supernatural" and "transcendent." As Otto expresses this quality:

> The truly 'mysterious' object is beyond our apprehension and comprehension, not only because our knowledge has certain irremovable limits, but because in it we come upon something inherently 'wholly other,' whose kind and character are incommensurable with our own, and before which we therefore recoil in a wonder that strikes us chill and dumb. (page 28)

We are reminded of St. Paul's exclamation, "How unsearchable are his judgments and how inscrutable his ways!" (Rom. 11:33)

The second attribute of the *numinous mysterium* is its element of *fascination.* The other four qualities which have been described might suggest that the natural reaction to the *mysterium tremendum* would be one of recoil and escape from it. The elements of awe and fear, overpoweringness, and otherness would all seem to be of a character which would impel men to turn away from the experience of the numinous and to avoid it as fully as possible. This, however, is not the case, and it is this element of fascination which accounts for it. In every genuine numinous experience there is always present a profound attraction toward its object; an inner thrill of excitement which results in a deep longing and powerful desire for that whose mysterious presence is so entrancingly sensed. One passage from Otto's description of this quality is particularly well expressed:

> The daemonic-divine object may appear to the mind an object of horror and dread, but at the same time it is no less something that allures with a potent charm, and the creature, who trembles before it, utterly cowed and cast down, has always at the same time the impulse to turn to it, nay even to make it somehow his own. The 'mystery' is for him not merely something to be wondered at, but something that entrances him; and besides that in it which bewilders and confounds, he feels a something that captivates and transports him with a

strange ravishment, rising often enough to the pitch of dizzy intoxication. (page 31)

This brief résumé will serve to give some notion of Otto's method of attack on this problem and of the spirit in which he engaged in his inquiry. It will also be sufficient, we hope, to indicate that in our quest for access to external reality we must, if we are to escape the danger of deceiving ourselves, treat all valid human experience with full respect. This involves recognizing the integrity and significance of those elements of our experience which we are unable to conceptualize with the same degree of seriousness which we are accustomed to accord to our conceptual experience. The experiences which Otto designates by the word "numinous" as well-nigh universal in all human cultures from the most primitive to the most advanced, and from the mists of prehistory to the present time. They pervade deeply all human literature and art, and the urge to share them with others has been responsible for some of the finest examples of poetic expression in all ages. Anyone who has read Emily Bronte's *Wuthering Heights,* Coleridge's *Kubla Khan,* or his *The Rime of the Ancient Mariner,* the poetry of Blake or Poe, the essays of John Ruskin, or Goethe's *Faust* and other writings, will do well at this point to pause and reflect on the status of those elements within them which were awakened and given response in his reading. Certainly, the sweeping denial of any possible external reference for this whole range of bona fide human experience, which is so often made in the name of science, on the clearly arbitrary a priori determination that only the conceptual elements of our experience can correspond to external reality, represents a tragically narrow and wholly arbitrary restriction on the range of our apprehension of the actual world which we inhabit.

The arbitrary and wholly unwarranted character of such a restriction is evident in an extreme degree in many of our contemporary studies of primitive societies and cultures, and in the majority of work carried out in the science of comparative religion. Here the bias for an exclusive concern with the conceptual and propositional often results in destroying the kind of intuitive sympathy with the subject under investigation which is essential to any adequate understanding of it. Indeed, the situation is remarkably reminiscent of the difficulties experienced by a small boy trying to comprehend and account for the behavior of an older brother or sister who has fallen in love for the first time. The detached and dispassionate search for the "bases" and "sources" of primitive religious experience in purely conceptual terms, which often governs such studies, has the effect of alienating the investigator from the very experience which it is his object to understand. The attempt to understand any experience of the holy within the limitations imposed by a strict adherence to contemporary standards of acceptable scientific explanation must begin with the a priori assumption that all non-conceptual elements in the experience are necessarily wholly subjective and unreal. Such an assumption, however, empties the experience of most of its content, and diverts the investigation of it from its proper object of trying to understand it to one of attempting to explain it away. Moreover, the investigator is forced by these assumptions into seeming to take a superior and condescending air toward his subject, so that all of his explanations involve him unavoidably in implying unfavorable comparisons between the inadequacy of primitive superstition and the sure ability of modern science. A great deal of both value and dignity could be restored to such studies simply by readmitting the essential validity and integrity of non-conceptual experience. Not only would this make it possible for the investigator to recapture a real sympathy for the range of human experience which he presumes to study, but it would also restore that necessary reference to external reality which alone can provide the experiences under investigation with a proper object.

The Non-conceptual in Science

It is not only in the category of the holy that we come upon the validity and reality of non-conceptual elements in experience. An obvious area, already noted, in which essentially the same kind of considerations apply is that of the category of the beautiful. We do not, however, have to confine the general idea to any specific category of experience, such as the holy or the beautiful, in order to see its fertility and usefulness. Once the essential idea that the whole process of concept formation is one in which we extract partial elements capable of conceptualization out of a more comprehensive matrix of experience has been clearly developed, one can become aware of a non-conceptual residuum left behind in every area of one's experience. This has become particularly clear to me in the case of science itself. Every one of the sciences is, for those who engage in it, shot through with experiences of great power and primary validity which never enter into the conceptual scheme that it is the primary task of the science to elaborate.

Consider, for example, the total experience of an astronomer who night after night is drawn back to the observatory for another session with the stars. There is surely much more here which delights and fascinates him than he can ever record in his data book. Biologists experience elements of reality in the direct observation of living systems through their microscopes which they are quite unable to reduce to conceptual symbols and express in the texts or treatises which they write. Yet such experiences are an essential part of the satisfactions and excitement of the actual conduct of research in biology. I am always impressed, when I am in a laboratory where experimental physics is being done, by the concrete reality of these non-conceptual overtones of what is actually being experienced by those who are working there. In the presence of a nuclear reactor in operation a profound sense of mystery and awe comes over one, and all the more intensely the more one knows conceptually about what is taking place in it. The same can be said about the experience of those who work around the great high-energy particle accelerators when the beam is on, and all around the target the strange assortment of short-lived mesons and hyperons are being continually born. The lone researcher with his spectrometer, his X-ray diffraction apparatus, or his liquid helium cryostat knows a love for his equipment and an inner excitement in the collection of data from it which he rarely, if ever, speaks of, but which you can sense when he shows it to you and explains what he is studying. In all of these cases that which astronomy, or biology, or physics is all about is actually happening before one's eyes. To paraphrase Job, that which heretofore one has heard about with one's ears, is here present, taking place, known and experienced in direct, face-to-face confrontation. In this situation the whole conceptual structure, which it has been the task of science to painstakingly construct, is seen to be only a framework or skeleton which is now filled out with its non-conceptual complement so as to become the total reality of which it was only a partial image. In the scientist's actual experience of this total reality, there resides among and between the interstices of this conceptual framework a whole range of experience which is incapable of conceptualization or scientific formulation, but which is just as real and, indeed, of the same elemental quality as the part of the experience out of which the conceptual framework is extracted.

These non-conceptual elements in the experience of engaging in science are of supreme importance in the teaching of science. It is, of course, possible to teach the whole conceptual content and structure of any science without ever taking the students into a laboratory. No teacher who has himself had the experience of engaging in the enterprise of his science is, however, ever satisfied with such an approach. Moreover, it is a mistake to suppose that the purpose of laboratory experiments in science teaching is primarily one of developing familiarity with apparatus and with the methodology and techniques involved. Of much greater importance is the direct confrontation of nature by the student in situations which permit the conceptual content of the science to be known and experienced within its total context in nature herself. Only thus can the teacher share with his students the non-conceptual, and therefore non-teachable, content of his science, and permit them to experience for themselves something of the excitement and delight of it. In the study of the image of science and scientists among high school students to which we referred in the second chapter, it is just this aspect of the scientific enterprise which is almost completely missing. Without it, science seems coldly analytical, impersonal, uninviting, and even dull. With it, however, science comes alive and acquires a fascination of such potency that many men and women have gladly devoted their whole lives and energies to it and have found in so doing the utmost in the way of personal satisfaction and reward.

The way in which all that is experienced in science exceeds the conceptual portion which constitutes the proper content of the science as a subject has been well expressed by Harold Schilling, from whom I have already quoted in a different context in the opening chapter. In commenting on the statement, "When you understand all about the sun and all about the atmosphere and all about the rotation of the earth, you may still miss the radiance of the sunset," which he quotes from Whitehead's *Science and the Modern World,* he says:

> At first glance these words seem trivial. Actually, however, they are deeply penetrating, for they suggest that our problem lies at the very foundations of knowledge: man's elemental abilities—and *inabilities* —to see and hear, to know and understand, to experience and live, to be sensitive and responsive to reality beyond himself. But more than that, they remind us of what all of us must surely realize in our more thoughtful and uninhibited moments that there is much more to be seen in the sunset than is revealed through the eyes of natural science.

In the volume of essays by the physicist Werner Heisenberg there is an account (pp. 60-76) of the famous controversy between Newton and Goethe on the theory of light and color, which provides an illuminating specific example of the aspect of science which we have been attempting to elucidate here. Newton, the scientist, approached his inquiry into this phenomenon with a determination to identify all of the conceptual elements contained in it which might be propositionally relatable to each other in the form of universal laws. In order to pursue his quest it was necessary for him to confine and profoundly restrict the phenomenon under investigation by compelling a general illumination to pass through narrow slits, and forcing the beam so formed into tortuous and complex paths and subjecting it to radical convolutions. There can, of course, be no question now about the enormous fruitfulness of this approach to an understanding of the phenomenon of light. Yet at the same time, as Heisenberg points out, it must be admitted that a blind man can learn all of physical optics, electromagnetic theory, and quantum electrodynamics without ever having any direct experience of the phenomenon he has concerned himself with explaining.

Goethe, the poet, on the other hand, was concerned to preserve the immediate contact with "living" nature in which resides all of the non-conceptual elements in our experience of it. The source of his interest in the problem seems to have arisen in the course of a stay in Italy when the vivid colors of the landscape captured his imagination and his interest, and this he vividly described in his diary. To him Newton's methods and approach to understanding the phenomenon which interested them both, were totally destructive of those aspects which for him were most real in it and lay closest to what required understanding. It is tempting for the modern mind to render a too simple verdict on the outcome of this controversy by relegating Goethe's theory to the category of the subjective and, therefore without doubt, illusory realm of experience, while regarding Newton's theory as objective and, therefore by modern standards, real. But this is merely to give expression to the innate bias toward the conceptual which we are here attempting to cure. As Heisenberg points out, Goethe's approach was from his standpoint as objective in intent as was Newton's from his. Heisenberg goes on to say,

> . . . it would be a . . . mistake to believe that the poet Goethe had more interest in arousing a vivid impression of the world than in acquiring a real understanding of it. Every genuinely great work of creative writing transmits real understanding of all aspects of life otherwise difficult to grasp. This is especially true of a work like his theory of color which must transmit new understanding and is written with full claims to scientific accuracy. (page 67)

The Supernatural as a Higher Dimension

Closely associated with the ideas of the spirit, of the holy, and of the beautiful is the idea of the transcendent and the supernatural. Indeed, wherever the objective status of our non-conceptual experience has been asserted or implied here, the question of a supernatural domain of reality has inevitably been raised implicitly. It seems well to turn now to an explicit treatment of this question. It is especially important to do this because of the widespread rejection of the supernatural in contemporary thought on the grounds that there is no scientific evidence for it. This, however, is equivalent to the axiomatic assumption about our experience, whose arbitrary and unwarranted character we have already sufficiently discussed, that only its conceptual component has any reference in objective reality, relegating its non-conceptual component to the realm of mere subjective feelings. What we must be brought to understand is that "nature" by definition consists in that aspect of reality which a human experiencing subject can conceptualize; all the rest is by definition "supernature." If, therefore, it became possible to obtain scientific evidence for some aspect of reality which had previously been regarded as supernatural, that element would necessarily immediately become a part of nature, and no one would thereafter classify it as a part of supernature. To reject the supernatural on the grounds of a lack of scientific evidence for it is, therefore, either a contradiction in terms or else a wholly unwarranted restriction on the character of external reality which insists that it has to be scientific in order to exist.

My own thinking about this matter has been much clarified by approaching it from the standpoint of Kant's identification of three-dimensional space and time as necessary requirements for any concept which is accessible to human intuition. In using this idea I do not mean to imply a commitment to the whole of Kant's epistemology, but only to extract this particular notion from it as a fruitful way of dealing with the boundary between the conceptual and the non-conceptual in human experience. Any object which is not a part of ordinary space and time could not, according to Kant's categories, be conceived by the human mind and could not, therefore, be a possible object for our conceptual experience. This requirement does not, however, exclude such an entity from being a possible object for *any kind* of human experience. Insofar as there exists a bona fide category of the non-conceptual, such an entity could well become a proper object for this kind of experience.

The German theologian Karl Heim, in his book *Christian Faith and National Science,* has made very effective use of this approach in a discussion of the status of the supernatural and the transcendent within the context of modern thought forms. Much of our modern difficulty with these notions arises from the vestigial imagery which helped men of former ages give substance and content to these essentially numinous experiences by picturing the natural world as sandwiched between heaven, whose boundaries began somewhere among the clouds, and hell, which lay deep under the earth. From the vantage point of our present view of the universe, this imagery is, of course, completely inadmissible and, indeed, false. But here we must be very cautious; for the imagery is not the equivalent of the non-conceptual experience which it represents. But it is just this experience, not its conceptual image or symbol, which is designated by the words "supernatural" and "transcendent." These continue with unabated prevalence as very real constituents of actual human experience. What we need, therefore, is a new imagery appropriate to our present view and understanding of the world, not an arbitrary refusal to recognize the experience simply because the image which formerly gave substance to it is no longer possible for us.

Since Kant's day mathematics has made phenomenal progress. One fascinating element in this has been the development of the means for working out in great detail the geometric and analytic properties of spaces having any number of dimensions. Every mathematician is, of course, prevented by his own human limitations from forming an intuitive picture in his mind of any space of more than three dimensions. It has been discovered, however, that this is no barrier to the mathematical deduction of all of the properties of such a space to an extent fully equal to that with which the properties of two- or three-dimensional space can be mathematically deduced. Against the background of these developments in mathematics, Heim has been able to develop a new conceptional image or symbol of the relationship between the natural and the supernatural by means of which we can again organize our experience of the supernatural without doing violence to our present enormously expanded knowledge of the physical universe.

The key to this approach lies in conceiving the whole space-time continuum of our human intuition as being immersed in a space of higher dimensions. This is exactly what is done in mathematics in studying the properties of a space of any given number of dimensions. Thus, in order to study the properties of the linear space represented by a circle, one draws it on a two-dimensional space such as a piece of paper. With reference to the plane of the paper, one can then deal with such properties of circles as radii, tangents, curvature, and the like. In the same way, in order to study the properties of the two-dimensional space represented by the surface of a sphere, one must view the sphere from the vantage point of three-dimensional space by suspending or immersing it in such a space. The mathematical properties of a space of n dimensions are obtained in the same way by considering it to be immersed in a space of $n + 1$ dimensions. As soon, however, as we form the notion of our whole material universe as being suspended in a space of higher dimensions, we at the same time gain an appreciation for the contingency of the particular universe which it has been given us to inhabit. Why, we are led to ask, should the space we have been given to know have precisely three, rather than two, four, or any other number of dimensions? Why was the particular combination of one temporal and three spatial dimensions chosen for our world rather than any of the other combinations that apparently might equally well have been selected?

Questions such as these naturally lead to the related question of why it should be that all that exists would have to be confined to one temporal and three spatial dimensions? The moment this question is raised in the context of the mathematical notion of a space immersed in one of higher dimensions, however, the thought immediately arises that perhaps reality is not really so restricted. In that event the supernatural domains of heaven and hell, which have been so universally acknowledged in human experience, have as much claim on reality as does the restricted spacio-temporal domain which constitutes nature. The only difference is that the boundary between the natural and the supernatural is then rather differently drawn, and in a manner much more aggreeable to modern views of the natural universe. Heaven, instead of being above us in ordinary space, is perpendicular to ordinary space, and the eternal is perpendicular to the temporal dimension. The transcendent and the supernatural, instead of being pushed farther and farther away from us with each new advance in astronomy, are again everywhere in immediate contact with us, just as the dimension perpendicular to a plane surface is everywhere in contact with it, though transcendent to it.

Heim makes particularly effective use, in this connection, of a romance published many years ago by Edwin Abbott, *Flatland*. All the inhabitants of Flatland are plane figures bounded by lines enclosing areas, in place of surfaces enclosing volumes as in three-dimensional space. They live in houses which have lines for walls and they enter into relationships with each other and live under limitations which are a source of much amusement for three-dimensional readers of the story. A visitor from Spaceland is able to appear suddenly and to become invisible at will simply by moving out into the third dimension, to which the inhabitants of Flatland have no access. In summarizing the significance of this story for our concept of the transcendent, Heim observes,

> The special significance of the story, *Flatland*, lies precisely in the fact that it demonstrates clearly that we are confined within the space in which we find ourselves when we enter into our existence, as though in a prison from which we cannot escape. The inhabitants of Flat-

land can, of course, as the story says, *believe* in a third dimension. They may, like the fictitious author of the tale, allow themselves, for the sake of this belief in the third dimension, to be sentenced by the supreme court of the Flatlanders to lifelong confinement in . . . an asylum. They may also dream of this more comprehensive space. But they *cannot* see it. (page 139)

I would add to this only that we can equally well imagine that the Flatlanders might be able to *experience* entities of three dimensional Spaceland although they would be unable, because of the limitations of their two-dimensional intuitions, to form concepts of such entities. All such experience would be necessarily non-conceptual, though none the less real.

Such an image, which sees the space-time continuum of the natural world as a contingent, restricted framework, immersed or suspended in a larger framework of higher dimension, is admirably suited to accommodate the Biblical view of reality. The essence of the supernatural in Biblical terms is its immediate and intimate contact with the natural at every point and every moment. Wherever one may be in ordinary space, one is surrounded by the reality of things invisible and unseen which, although incapable of conceptual definition as objects of the world of nature, are nevertheless just as real and immediately present. It is illuminating to read Psalm 139 with this thought in mind. When one considers the totality of any experience, including in it besides that which can be defined and captured within space and time, also that of beauty, of holiness, and of the spirit, which is ineffable, then one can see immediately by means of this image how the experienced reality simply intersects space and time. That portion of the total reality lying within the intersection we call natural, and our experience of it is conceptual; the remainder lying outside we call "supernatural," and our experience of it is non-conceptual. In a world of three dimensional objects, a plane would pass through some of them and completely miss others. The former would, just as for the Flatlanders, have both natural and supernatural aspects, whereas the latter would be wholly supernatural. This distinction would not, however, be a property of the objects themselves, but only of the plane which might or might not intersect them. What we call natural is only that aspect of reality which happens to lie within the space in which we are confined; all the rest is supernatural. In that case, however, the supernatural is just as real, and indeed of the same quality in itself, as the natural. Moreover, it is everywhere in immediate contact with it and an integral part of it. The distinction between natural and supernatural lies in us and the limitations imposed by our finite intuitions; not in reality itself. All this conforms nicely with the Biblical views of the character of reality on the one hand, and of the boundary between nature and supernature on the other.

The Structure of Matter

There is another approach to the reality of the transcendent through modern physics and mathematics which is quite different in character from the one based on space and time which has just been described. This approach might best be characterized as arising out of the classical "atomic quest" of the ancients. Long before the era of modern science the hope, which it has so largely realized, of finding the means to explain the variety and diversity of natural phenomena in terms of the variety of combinations and associations of a limited number of elementary constituents of matter called "atoms," had been clearly formulated and expressed. Anyone who today reads the works of Leucippus, Democritus, and Lucretius cannot fail to be impressed with the extent to which their hopes and program for a rational understanding of the diversity of phenomena have been actualized. With a real minimum of empirical data with which to substantiate their hypothesis, what they foresaw was the possibility of understanding the whole range of physical reality and phenomena in terms of the combinations which could be entered into by a few simple and elementary constituents of matter called "atoms." These atoms would themselves possess none of the secondary properties of matter, such as color, taste, odor, elasticity, durability, or roughness. Instead, all such properties would be seen under analysis to arise from the various associations into which such atoms would enter. The solid, liquid, and gaseous states of matter would ultimately be seen to be merely the result of several basic ways in which such atoms could associate themselves. Solid matter could be either hard or soft, brittle or pliable, durable or easily eroded, depending on the nature of such associations. All in all, when we compare their expectations, and the grounds on which they advanced them, against our present understanding of the structure of all matter and the nature of all material phenomena in terms of the associations of electrons, protons, and neutrons in atomic nuclei, atoms, and molecules, we cannot fail to be amazed at the depth of their insight and the extent to which their expectations have been confirmed.

Against this background of appreciation for their remarkable achievement in the face of such meager evidence, we are constrained to inquire in what ways, if any, they failed to appreciate some basic aspects of our modern detailed development of the total program they foresaw and longed to carry out. In response to such a question we can point to many details in which they failed to appreciate the exact manner in which modern theories account for aspects of reality which they hoped might be understandable in terms of atoms. These, however, are matters only of detailed knowledge and do not affect their fundamental expectations. There is really only one aspect in which modern science has departed radically from and, indeed, gone beyond their basic expectations of what an atomic theory might explain. This has to do with the properties retained by the elementary constituents, or "atoms," themselves. The basic hope of the ancients was to understand all secondary properties such as color, taste, durability, hardness, etc., from different associations of elementary atoms which themselves would possess none of these properties. At the same time they never questioned, however, that these atoms must continue to possess a certain minimum of basic primary qualities such as size, shape, position, and mass. Indeed, they thought of their atoms as invisible solid particles of assorted shapes and sizes in continual motion but occupying at every instant a definite point in space. It is just in this distinction between primary qualities possessed by the atoms, and secondary qualities emerging out of their associations, that modern developments have failed to confirm their expectations.

Until just a few decades ago, all the modern developments in the atomic theory of matter supported the ancient atomists in this respect. About forty years ago, however, further elaboration of the theory was balked. Little further progress could be made until the radical transformation of classical mechanics into quantum mechanics had been accomplished. Thereafter progress was phenomenal and certainly has far exceeded in elegance, simplicity, and comprehensiveness even the wildest expectations of earlier researchers. Now the surprising thing about this phenomenal progress as compared to traditional expectations is that, in a very basic and proper sense, it can all be said to have been made possible by abandoning the requirement that the elementary constituents of matter must themselves continue to possess the "primary" qualities of size, shape, and position. For in quantum mechanics electrons, protons, and neutrons no longer can be assigned any size or shape, and because of the uncertainty principle they cannot any longer even be conceived as occupying a position in space. Atomic nuclei, atoms, molecules, and crystals made up of combinations of these particles have definite and measurable sizes and shapes. But these all arise out of the character of the forces which these elementary particles exert on each other and the motions which they execute in response to these forces. The particles themselves possess none of these properties.

The only "primary" properties which these "elementary" particles, together with the strange assortment of other recently discovered particles, can still be said to possess are the basic substantive ones of mass, electric charge, and nuclearity together with the dynamical and symmetrical properties of spin, lifetime, and parity. The very fact of the existence of these properties in the particular combinations in which they occur—among the variety of elementary particles so far discovered—has become the primary problem of physics. It is inevitable that the question should arise as to why each of these particles possesses just exactly the rest mass which always characterizes it, and no other. The masses and lifetimes of these particles form a spectrum of discrete values with wide gaps between each value. Why these particular values and no others? What significance does this particular spectrum of discrete numbers have as the one adopted in nature to govern the particular forms in which matter can occur? These are the fundamental questions which pose themselves with great insistence to contemporary physicists.

Whether it will prove possible to find an answer to these fundamental questions we, of course, cannot know. If and when it is found, the answer will certainly constitute the next great fundamental advance in physics. Moreover, we are also justified in anticipating that it will probably represent the ultimate resolution of the atomic problem as it was conceived and proposed long ago by the ancients. For it will necessarily involve the discovery and definition of a still more elementary particle, or entity, whose various states correspond to the presently observed particulate manifestations of matter. From a knowledge of the structure and properties of this truly elementary entity, it will be possible to show how and why each one of the strange assortment of particles which we now know to exist occurs in nature. The sequence of particles, called *fermions,* which in order of ascending mass are called the neutrino, electron, muon, proton, neutron, lambda-particle, sigma-particles, and cascades, as well as the corresponding sequence of so-called *bosons* which in the same order are called the photon, pions, and K-mesons, would all emerge as elements in this new theory and be seen, together with their specific masses, charges, lifetimes, spins, and parities, to be consequences of the single elementary entity whose possible states both explain and give rise to this spectrum of discrete particles.

Once such a step is taken, we will be able to start with whatever elementary physical entity the new theory defines, and from it obtain, first, the particular particles listed above, together with their specific physical properties as they are now known. From these we will then single out the neutron and proton, together with the forces between them which are determined by the pion, and by means of these explain how all the nuclei of the atoms are formed. To this collection of nuclei, we will then be able to add the electron, together with the electric force which holds it to the positively charged nucleus as determined by the photon, and explain how all the atoms of chemical elements are formed as well as their detailed sizes, forces, and other properties. With this information we can then go on, as a next step, to explain how all of the possible molecules and crystalline solids are formed from the various possible combinations of these atoms as determined by the chemical valence forces between them, which in turn have already arisen out of and been determined by the pattern of the electrons in each of the atoms. Clearly the fulfillment of this program, which has already been largely accomplished in detail except for the first step mentioned above, would represent the complete fruition of the dream so hopefully advanced long ago in the *De Rerum Natura* of Lucretius.

With this setting for the resolution of the atomic theory of matter in mind, let us turn to a consideration of the character of the hypothetical elementary physical entity on which it would all depend. The first thing we can say about it is that it will not itself possess such tangible properties as mass, electric charge, lifetime, and spin, which are all that remain as intuitively discernible properties of the so-called elementary particles as we now know them. Each of these properties of each particle will emerge from the theory as a solution of the problem why the particular spectrum of such particles occurs in nature. It is essential to the adequacy of such a theory that the elementary entity which accounts for these particularities should not itself possess them since, otherwise, it could not really explain them. Thus, whatever this elementary entity may turn out to be, we can be fairly confident that it will not itself possess any property or quality which characterizes our immediate experience of matter. Not only will it not possess the properties of size, shape, and position—which have already been denied to the presently recognized elementary constituents of matter—but it will also have lost the few remaining experiential properties which they still retain. Indeed, compelling expectations from theoretical physics lead us to anticipate that it will not be an object in space and time at all. As such, it will be represented, defined, and dealt with only as an abstract mathematical entity, incapable of being pictured or imagined by the mind even as one of the multi-dimensional abstract spaces already familiar to mathematicians.

This observation brings us to the point of this long, and seemingly unrelated, diversion from our main concern—the reality of non-conceptual experience. The point, actually, should have been an obvious one all along, even to the ancients. For what even they proposed to do in their embryonic atomic theories was to account for the variety and diversity of observable phenomena in terms of simpler elements which would not themselves possess the varied properties of that which they were designed to explain. What they should have realized, but did not, however, is that the distinction they made between primary and secondary properties of matter was a wholly artificial one, bound to be eliminated when tested experimentally. For the logic of the theory that atoms possess any experiential property such as size, shape, position, or mass made it inevitable that men should question why any atom possesses the given property under discussion and not some slightly different one. As soon, however, as this question is raised and an explanation for it found, it is clear that whatever will be the more basic entity which explains the particular property in question, it will not itself possess that property. Pursuing this line of reasoning step by step, we see that the only possible ultimate solution of the atomic quest will be to arrive at a really elementary component of all matter which, while accounting completely for all the manifold diversity of matter and its associated phenomena as we observe and experience it, will not itself possess any observable property whatever.

This rather inevitable conclusion, however, simply brings us by a very circuitous route to an assertion about the material, space-time universe which Biblical doctrine has, on quite different grounds, always maintained about it—namely, that the reality on which it is contingent and on which it depends for its entire existence lies outside and beyond it, or, in other words, is transcendent to it. In projecting the course of scientific explanation to its ultimate fruition, I myself do not see that any other conclusion than this is possible. Moreover, this conclusion is in reality simple and straightforward and not really at all so complicated, and seemingly dependent on, abstruse considerations from mathematical physics, as the long preparation leading up to it may seem to have implied. It is simply the old assertion in a different guise of the contingency of all created things. The explanation of why the universe is the way it is and not some other way—why molecules, atoms, neutrons, protons, and electrons are specifically what they are, or why there are just three dimensions of space and one of time—the reasons for all this special particularity of creation must obviously be sought for outside creation. It is only our momentary enthusiasm over each new partial step towards, and achievement in, understanding nature which has given us a kind of myopia, preventing us from looking beyond the partial stage we have reached at any given moment to see the ultimate goal toward which the enterprise in which we were engaged has been inevitably leading us.

This outcome of the course of scientific explanation is an inevitable consequence of the endeavor to understand nature. Without any conscious effort or intent on the part of scientists, every pathway of understanding within nature must, if pursued long enough, ultimately lead beyond nature. The ultimate explanation for that which is confined within space and time must be sought for outside space and time. The ground of existence of every finite being lies beyond itself. Because this is so, the course of the scientific explanation of nature will finally lead beyond nature into supernature. For a long time, to be sure, science had so much of the inner structure and fabric of nature herself to uncover and interrelate, that it seemed in its early stages that it might well go on forever exploring within nature without ever being led beyond her special confines. But this, as we know now, was only apparent. With each new stage of understanding a new set of questions emerged directed at the character of the underlying reality upon which that stage rested. In seeking the answers to such questions, a still deeper level of reality was revealed. Ultimately it was impossible to avoid arriving at a point where the next underlying stage would go right through the boundary of space-time. Once the scientific enterprise was launched, there was no possibility of keeping it confined. By the inherent character of its own inner dynamics, like a chick embryo gradually building into itself the unorganized material available to it within the egg, it was inevitable that science would in time grow to the point where the shell would break, and would burst the confines of the natural to emerge into the wider realities of that which transcends nature.

It is not only in the area of the elementary constituents of matter that modern science is being led beyond the confines of the natural into the transcendent. Modern cosmology also, in tracing out the history of the universe and determining its age, is equally well being led inevitably toward a crossing of the space-time boundary. Historical geology and paleontology had a major task to perform in tracing backward to the Cambrian, and somewhat earlier periods, the long history of the crust of this planet. For a time that seemed a large enough and startling enough task in itself, without concerning oneself too much about what came before. But now we go all the way back to a turbulent mass of gas and dust before there was any earth or sun, or planets at all, and attempt to see how all these originated as the cloud contracted under its own gravity. So, too, with all the other stellar systems in our own galaxy, as well as with those in all the others besides. With the help of the expanding universe and the built-in clocks of natural radioactive materials such as uranium and thorium, we now attempt to go still farther backwards in time to an epoch when the gas and dust was itself formed by chemical combination from a mixture of elementary atoms. In recent years we have even attempted to penetrate the mists of time still more, and to go back to a stage when there were not even any atoms, but only neutrons or protons out of which the present atoms condensed. But from that stage, the next step or two backwards in time inevitably leads us right out of space-time into that which transcends nature. One arrives at a moment in history when that which had not before been in nature took up its existence in nature: the moment when neutrons or protons, or perhaps some kind of hyperons which decay into them, came into being and started a history in time; or the moment when the expanding universe entered upon its existence and that expansion which has been characteristic of it ever since; or when the initial combinations of neutrons and protons which constitute uranium and thorium were formed, only to decay slowly away into isotopes of lead ever since.

All these contemporary theories are highly speculative and uncertain, but they all in one way or another take the history of nature back to a time when the next earlier stage must have had its origin outside of nature. Whichever pathway of understanding one takes, one is ultimately led to such a moment. In a universe in which the second law of thermodynamics holds there is no other way out. Along any historic path backwards in time one chooses to follow, one comes upon a sequence of irreversible transformations which ultimately leads to a beginning; to a moment, that is, at which something which had not existed in space-time takes up an existence within space-time. The history of the universe is not a tale told by an idiot which simply runs on and on. One cannot push it backwards along any route without finally coming to some event which transcends nature and thus leads out of nature toward the supernatural ground upon which the existence of all finite created things must rest. The origin and source of all that exists within space and time must ultimately be sought for outside space and time. This should have been obvious all along, but at the stage which science has now reached, it is a conclusion which can no longer be avoided even by those who would still prefer not to acknowledge it.

Summary

What then have we accomplished in this chapter? Really only two simple, but very fundamental, things. Giving them in the reverse order from that in which we introduced them, we have shown that the contingency of nature implies that which is transcendent to nature—namely, the existence and reality of supernature. Secondly, we have shown that our human experience of reality divides itself both naturally and properly, as attested throughout the whole combined witness to that experience of the human race, into conceptual and non-conceptual components. The former is the proper domain of science, which has the object of understanding what we term "nature." The latter is the proper domain of religion and poetry, which have the object of understanding what we term "supernature." In making these distinctions, however, we should never forget that they pertain solely to us and our own human limitations in experiencing and knowing reality beyond ourselves. The whole of reality as it is in itself, apart from our experience and knowledge of it, doubtless involves no such division or boundary between nature and supernature. Both reality and experience are unitary; it is only because of the peculiar limitations of the human mind, which is able to form concepts only out of portions of experience and leaves aside what it cannot conceptualize, that reality presents itself to our apprehension as partly natural and partly supernatural. This circumstance can hardly be taken, however, as it so often is, as justification for rejecting the latter as unreal and subjective, while retaining the former as real and objective.

One final word of caution must be stated, however, before we leave this topic. Whenever science leads us outside of nature into supernature, what it gives us is at best an abstract mathematical entity incapable of being visualized or represented by any conceptual model. It does not, nor in the nature of things can it, lead us to a knowledge of God, or even to a recognition of his existence. Dimensions perpendicular to space-time, such as may represent heaven, hell, and eternity, are in themselves merely formal mathematical constructions. The transcendental reality whose several manifestations are the spectrum of elementary particles (whatever that may turn out to be) will certainly be impersonal and abstrusely mathematical. Whatever preceded the entry into history of the neutrons and protons which now inhabit space and time is likely to continue to be enigmatic or, as least, abstract and purely formal, in any science of the future. None of this is even particularly religious in character, to say nothing of leading to any kind of knowledge of God. As we shall see in Chapter VI, we are absolutely dependent for our knowledge of God on his initiative in revealing himself to us through Israel and Christ. It is a forlorn and impossible hope which so many have today that man, working on his own initiative by means of science alone, may somehow eventually find God. All he can possibly discover in this way is something inscrutable which can only be expressed in abstract mathematics. No one can ever be led to Christ by such a route. God cannot be known by his creature man except inso-far as he has chosen to reveal himself to man. But such revelation is an entirely different thing from science.

V

Knowledge

MANY OF THE matters with which we have been concerned in previous chapters raise the question of what it is possible for us to know. When we speak of such things as the spirit, the beautiful, or the holy, are we speaking of aspects of reality about which it is possible in any meaningful sense to have knowledge? If we should feel that this question can be answered in the affirmative, then a further question arises about the character of such knowledge. How, for example, does the knowledge we claim to have of the holy compare with the knowledge we have of physical nature? Are these two forms of knowledge of a fundamentally different character, or is it necessary, in order for both of them to be true knowledge, that they should ultimately be capable of being reduced to the same basis and to be known by the same means? These questions are an indication of the way in which the problem of knowledge—the subject of this chapter—arises insistently in connection with every other problem which we have raised and attempted to deal with.

Another way to express the same problem is in terms of the contrast between the question of reality and the question of knowledge. These two questions correspond to the two alternative paths of inquiry into any given class of phenomena. In Chapter III, for example, we considered the question of the reality of spirit. The intent there was to isolate and examine those aspects of life in community which we designate by the word "spirit." This we attempted to do in such a way that the idea of spirit would emerge from the discussion as a distinct and recognizable element in our common experience and that we would apprehend it as a component of the real world set over against us as experiencing subjects. In Chapter IV we did much the same with the idea of the holy. In both cases we were concerned with the question of the reality of the phenomena under consideration. To deal with this question we had only to identify a common source for a particular type of human experience.

The other pathway of inquiry into either of these subjects opens before us when we raise the question of what we can really know about them and by what means such knowledge is to be obtained. This question is, in many ways, a much more demanding and difficult one than the question of their reality. The usual thing is to simply take for granted the reality of that which is experienced in common. This is as true of science as it is of any other category of human experience. The working scientist takes for granted the reality of the world which he investigates and does not raise the question as to whether the knowledge of the world which science is in process of accumulating actually represents the world as it really is. Scientists are often very impatient and unsympathetic with philosophers of science who do raise such questions; even with those whose objective is to support the validity of scientific knowledge. On the other hand, the experiences in physics of the last half-century have introduced an air of tentativeness about the degree to which our knowledge in this most basic of all the sciences can be depended upon to reflect the actual structure of the real world. We have seen some of the basic understandings of the classical Newtonian mechanics discarded and replaced by quite different concepts, first by the relativistic mechanics of Einstein and then, later, by quantum mechanics. As a result of these experiences the question arises about our present knowledge in physics—whether some other equally drastic revolution, radically transforming physics, may not be in store for us in the future. To paraphrase the urgently important question asked of our Lord: Is the understanding of physical reality which we now possess what we have been seeking, or do we look for another? The extraordinary difficulty of giving an answer to this question with any degree of assurance shows how much more difficult is the problem of knowledge than the problem of reality.

When we turn from knowledge in the sciences to such aspects of reality as those designated by the words "spirit" and "holy," the problem of knowledge becomes much more difficult. Indeed, if we apply to them the same criteria which we employ to give validity to scientific knowledge, our only conclusion can be that we simply do not have any knowledge at all of such aspects of reality. To have knowledge of spirit in the way in which knowledge is had scientifically, means that spirit must be studied by the method and approach of sociology. But when this is done, the whole idea of spirit simply evaporates into a group of qualities and emotions. In sociological terms what we call "spirit" emerges merely as a complex of subjective psychological elements associated with group behavior and group dynamics. Indeed, in this way of knowing, the idea itself appears so derivative and so much a product of a complex of more elementary constituents that the word "spirit" is itself never used in scientific studies of group phenomena.

In like manner, as we have seen, the idea of the holy when subjected to scientific ways of knowing turns out to have essentially no conceptual content which could form an interrelated body of knowledge such as we have in science. If, therefore, we confine ourselves to the type of knowledge which is obtained in science, the best we can say of such an object as Otto's *mysterium tremendum* is that we can have no knowledge of it at all. Such a statement, however, is generally sufficient to dispose of the matter completely, for so great in our day is the prestige of science and of scientific ways of knowing that any aspect of reality not known by that method is, for the most part, treated as effectively unreal and illusory. Certainly any part of reality, which is of such a character as to be completely unknowable within the limitations of the finite human estate, might just as well not exist at all, so far as we are concerned. It is essentially on this basis, in terms of a theory of knowledge, that such aspects of reality as spirit, beauty, and the holy have been largely rejected and explained away as purely subjective manifestations of the human nervous system with no counterparts in external reality.

It is, therefore, my purpose here to attempt to delineate two independent ways of knowing which, I believe, are regularly exercised by all mankind in the common process of organizing and interpreting experience, but which, at the same time, are distinct from the way of knowing employed in science. In other words, I propose to recognize and describe two distinct forms of knowledge over and above the type which has largely been regarded in the modern forms of positivism, as well as in eighteenth- and nineteenth-century epistemology, as the only form of knowledge available to men. This is admittedly an ambitious project. If the objective were to develop such independent ways of knowing in anything like the detail with which standard conceptual knowledge has been studied, it would certainly be entirely too ambitious to undertake in so brief a space. My objective is, however, more modest, for what I purpose to do is to exhibit the possibility of these two independent modes of knowledge and to sketch their general character. No detailed analysis of the structure of either will be attempted.

The contrast between the accepted form of knowledge typified by science and the first of these independent modes was cited in the last chapter, where the distinction was developed in some detail between conceptual and non-conceptual experience. The chief difference between what was attempted there and what will primarily concern us here is the difference between the question of reality, as that which lies beyond us and stands over against us, and the question of knowledge, as that which we are able to develop reliably and consistently in our minds. There we were primarily concerned with the ontological question of that which exists apart from our own individual desires and aspirations, or of that whose reality is not contingent upon us and which would, therefore, continue to exist after we have ceased to be. Here the concern is with that which is inside us, with the way in which we organize and interpret our experience, with what we believe we can know about the world in which we are placed.

Rational Knowledge

When we speak of knowledge in the context of contemporary thought on the subject, what we have in mind is almost exclusively conceptual and rational knowledge. What is posited first is a perceiving, experiencing, observing subject who is the seat of such knowledge. Between this subject and the world that he perceives, experiences, and knows is a boundary, which can well be thought of as constituted by his skin, upon which impinges all the influences which give rise to his experience, and across which is transmitted everything which produces any kind of perception in the subject. This boundary separates the subject from the object, the category of the "subjective" from that of the "objective," that which is distinctively inside each one of us, and private, from that which is distinctively outside and public.

What we term our knowledge of the world is a mentally constructed fabric of identifications and interrelationships which slowly evolve for each individual in the process of understanding his experience. A child growing up on a farm very early forms a concept of "cow." At first, this concept is vague and shadowy, being formed out of only a few fleeting images or impressions in which a cow was first seen or heard. As the child's experience grows, however, his mental concept "cow" grows with it. Each new experience of seeing, touching, and hearing cows both add new content to the concept he has formed in his mind, and correct and modify it. At the same time the concept becomes related in more and more well-defined ways to other concepts, such as hay, milk, veal, beef, calf, bull, animal, hair, hide, tail, etc., which are developing simultaneously with it out of the child's growing store of experience. The myriad of interrelationships which so develop with all these other concepts serve to ever more clearly and distinctively set apart the concept "cow" from all other elements of the child's experience. It becomes a definite element in the child's knowledge of the world he inhabits, and a more and more meaningful tool for his interpretation and understanding of his experience of that world.

Before going on to consider modes of knowledge different from this familiar conceptual type, there are several aspects of it which should be brought out as background for that discussion. The first of these is the part played by the community, i.e., the family, of which the child is a part. It is within the communal unit of father, mother, brothers, and sisters that the process of concept formation is carried out. Each sense perception which the child has of a cow or of anything else is shared within this community. Innumerable questions are asked and answered, and in addition the older members of the family group purposely arrange and contrive additional experiences with cows which will assist the child in the formation of an increasingly valid and adequate concept in his mind with which to associate the word "cow." This is both by way of addition, in which new elements bearing on the concept are added to the child's experience, and also by way of correction, in which misunderstandings and erroneous notions are corrected by appropriate reference to new experience. In this way, first in the family, and later in school and the other communal associations of which he is a part, the child's experience is interpreted for him and given coherence by the community. From the scanty evidence available to us through the few instances of "wolf children," it would appear that the whole process of concept formation cannot take place at all apart from community. All knowledge comes through community, as we have already seen in the first two chapters.

The second aspect of knowledge relates to the capacity of the community to go well beyond the opportunities of each individual for direct perception of objects in the process of concept formation. A child could easily grow up in a large city without ever having an opportunity to see a cow. Nevertheless, by means of stories and verbal description, even without the aid of pictures and other audio-visual aids, he could be led by his community to form a reasonably adequate concept of such an animal. Then later during a drive through the country where he actually saw a cow, he would already possess a conceptual framework within which to assimilate the experience. This kind of event is always an occasion of considerable excitement. Even more striking examples of this same capacity occur in science where the painstaking construction of a conceptual image of reality, which the science community is engaged in developing, leads to the anticipation of some new and hitherto unsuspected element in the world, such as a new planet or an unknown atomic particle. When such an expectation is confirmed by actual observation of the predicted entity or phenomenon, the experience is always an exciting one.

Thirdly, I would emphasize the integrative character of every concept. It is a mistake to think of the concepts which we have in our minds as being directly related to a single act of perception of the corresponding object. Each direct perception of a cow which the child experiences is a partial, fleeting thing. The child immediately connects it, to be sure, with the concept "cow" which he already possesses. But the idea of a cow which he has in his mind is a complicated product of many previous experiences with the same animal which he has had in other contexts, together with stories about cows, discussions involving them, and answers to his questions concerning them which he has had with his family or at school. No single act of sense perception or of experience is sufficient for concept formation. All of our conceptual knowledge is the product of many experiences over a long period interpreted and understood through community.

Finally, I would emphasize the distinction between our store of conceptual knowledge and the objects and phenomena in the external world to which it refers. All of our experience, both directly of nature itself and indirectly through the medium of language in community, comes to us across the thin boundary of perception which separates us from the world "outside." All of our knowledge of that world is "inside." Our idea of a cow and the animal itself as an entity of the external world are forever separated from each other by this limiting boundary across which our experience flows into us. There is no way in which we can get out of our skins and know the existence of the animal independently of our experience of it. The only means we have for checking the validity of our conceptual knowledge is by means of a circuit which starts with the raw data of experience at this boundary, leads via appropriate correspondences to concepts, thence by rational manipulation of these concepts to some new conceptual pattern which, by reversing the correspondences between concept and experience, leads to the anticipation of new experience. The confirmation of such expectations in actual experience is the process of empirical validation, by means of which we all continuously correct, modify, and improve our conceptual image of reality. In a single perception there is no way in which we can tell the difference between a mirage and the "real" object which it appears to be. By such a process as that which has just been outlined, however, we can use our rational knowledge to suggest a whole chain of additional experiences of the same object which will ultimately either dispose of it as a mirage or confirm its objective existence for us.

Against this brief background of the character of conceptual knowledge we may introduce the question of other forms of knowledge in the following manner. To begin with we may note that there is a richness in immediate experience which is much impoverished in the process of conceptualization. When we extract all the rational elements out of our experience which can be symbolized as concepts, there is a large residuum left behind which represents that part of our experience about which we say that we "cannot find words to express it." With this much admitted, the customary epistemological position is to regard this residuum as an unformed and unmanageable mass of feelings, intuitions, and subjective states which is incapable of rising to the level of knowledge. In this view only the rational, conceptual distillation of our experience which can be dealt with in propositional form and subjected to empirical validation can properly be called knowledge. Even though spontaneous experience loses much of its fullness when symbolized and expressed, it is nevertheless in this view only that portion of it which is capable of being symbolized and thought about rationally which can be considered knowable.

Non-conceptual Knowledge

In order to find an alternative to this position, it is necessary to exhibit the possibility of dealing with, and sharing in community, residual components of experience in a way sufficiently analogous to that in which we manage our conceptual experience to make the same word "knowledge" applicable to it. The basis for doing so has, however, already been laid in the last chapter. We have already seen there an example of the possibility of dealing with one form of non-conceptual experience in a definite, describable, and sharable way. Let us explore here the possibilities which that example provides for the development of a theory of non-conceptual knowledge.

In order to make our discussion concrete let us consider the same child in whom we have already considered the development of the concept "cow" as an instance of the way in which conceptual knowledge is acquired. Now, however, let us suppose that this child in his wanderings about the farm comes upon some woodland glade, a portion of an old stone wall, or a bubbling brook, and there experiences a sense of overpowering awe and reverence, mixed with enchantment as from the mysteriously sensed presence of a great and holy spirit. He has had, in other words, a numinous experience which we know (as he cannot) is not capable, at that stage, of the same kind of development as was his initial experience of a cow. We must now ask ourselves whether there exists any kind of parallel development which, in the proper community, could ultimately come to fruition in a store of non-conceptual knowledge comparable to the more familiar store of conceptual knowledge.

In approaching an answer to this question the first observation to be made concerns the vital role which is played by the community of which the child is a part. If his family or school firmly disbelieves in the reality of anything which cannot be conceptualized, then every inquiry which the child makes or hints at in an effort to understand his numinous experience will be promptly discounted and passed off as a mere aberration. This will clearly establish a course of development in which the child learns to more and more effectively suppress his response to numinous experience, and so ultimately comes to share the conviction of his community that there is nothing outside himself to which such experience refers. There is no question but what every community has this kind of power over every kind of knowledge. A family which had very little to do with cows and which firmly disbelieved in their existence could deal with a child's occasional experiences of seeing or hearing a cow in the same way. By developing in him a conviction of the illusory and chimerical character of such experiences, he would acquire an entirely adequate capacity to suppress his response to them. Only later, when he left the family and became a part of some other community which did believe in cows, would his lost capacity of response to this segment of his experience be revived.

If, on the other hand, the family were one with a keen sensitivity to the reality of "things invisible and unseen," the return of the child from this first experience in woodland or field will be dealt with quite differently. This experience will be received with the same natural and unstrained acceptance as was his first experience of a cow. Thereafter, a long train of development will take place in which repeated and various numinous experiences of the child are integrated with those of the family into a fabric of non-conceptual knowledge shared in common among them, comparable in scope and diversity to their common store of conceptual knowledge. In mountain and field, sunset and empty sky, storm and lightning, and most especially at church in altar and sacrament, music and liturgy, Bible story and psalm, the world of spirit will emerge and come alive, and the child will come to share with the rest of the family the knowledge of the lovely mystery of presentness in the holy, just as naturally and fully as they share together the objects and happenings which make up the world they know rationally and conceptually.

In order to discuss the course of this development in a manner parallel to that in which we discussed the course of development of conceptual knowledge, we require a word to designate that in the mind which stands in the same relationship to numinous experience as the word "concept" stands in relationship to rational experience. I have sought rather extensively for such a word but so far have not come up with one which appeals to me. One possibility would be "noncept," but if it is necessary to invent a word for the purpose, one ought to be able to do much better than that. The best interim solution I have been able to find is "intuent," which means something known by intuition as opposed to that which is known by reason. Just as conceptual seeds can be planted in the mind which, nourished by a long and varied sequence of rational or intelligible experiences through the interpretive power of community, can grow and flower into fully developed concepts, so too non-conceptual seeds can be planted in the mind which, when similarly nourished by a long and varied sequence of numinous experiences through the interpretive power of community, can grow and flower into fully-developed intuents. An example of an intuent is Otto's "mysterium tremendum."

The seat and origin of all non-conceptual knowledge is identical with that of conceptual knowledge. It is that thin boundary layer, approximately coincident with our skins, in which perception takes place and at which our experience of the world around us originates. Out of the moment-by-moment stream of spontaneous experience originating in this boundary, the mind extracts some elements out of which it builds concepts, and others out of which it builds intuents. An analogy from photography comes to mind here. Using a special camera and special film sensitive only to infra-red radiation, a picture can be taken of an object using the heat radiation coming from it. When such a picture is compared with an ordinary photograph of the same object taken with visible light, the contrast is often quite striking. If we equate the object being photographed with external reality and our experience of the world with the total radiation coming from the object, then the process of extracting a rational component from experience can be compared to the sensitivity of standard film to visible light, and the extraction of a numinous component from the same experience can be compared to the sensitivity of infrared film to long wave-length heat radiation. The picture taken in the first instance is then a concept, while that taken in the second is an intuent.

It often happens that we form both a concept and an intuent of one and the same external reality. A central example of this is to be found in our concept of God. This concept is made up of little more than a collection of such rationally definable attributes as goodness, omnipotence, perfection, etc., as may be assigned to him. The concept alone, however, is unable to deal with his existence or presence, and is best represented by what we have in mind when we speak of the "God of philosophy." Our intuent of God, on the other hand, is by definition incapable of rational description or representation, but refers directly to the sensed reality of his presence and holiness and is best represented by that which comes to mind when we speak of the "living God." Yet the concept and the intuent are, as in our photographic analogy, different pictures of one and the same object taken by the light of two different fractions of our total experience of God. In this case, however, as we know from the experience of nineteenth-century deism, when we eliminate the intuent, the concept, like a cut flower, ultimately dries up and withers away. This, however, is not always the case, or even frequently the case, as we shall see from a different example.

We have made extensive use of the example of the farm

child's formation of the concept "cow." Let us now consider the same process of concept formation for "tiger" in the case of a child in some village in India or Africa where tigers are common. So far as the conceptual tiger is concerned, the process of concept formation will be identical with the process already described for the conceptual cow. In this case, however, there will also be, because of the nature of the animal, an equally full and ample numinous tiger in parallel with it, out of which the child is likely to form an intuent of a tiger just as real and vivid to him as his concept of a tiger. The concept, being rational, scientific, and dispassionate, will be neither inviting nor uninviting, but it will be quite useful to him. The intuent, on the other hand, being irrational, alive, and passionate, will be both terribly uninviting and fascinatingly inviting; but it will also be completely useless to him. In this case, however, if an exclusive concern with the rational and scientific, coupled with a deep-seated disbelief in the reality of everything which cannot be conceived by the human mind, results in eliminating completely the intuent "tiger," the concept "tiger" will, of course, continue to be fully operative and will be in no way diminished by the loss of the intuent.

The next question which arises is the manner in which non-conceptual knowledge can be communicated and shared in community. This becomes primarily the question of the way in which language can be employed for the sharing of such experience. We have already made a considerable point of the essential role played by community in the nurture and development of knowledge out of both rational and numinous experience. For this to be the case, however, it is clearly necessary for the members of the community to have some means of communicating with each other. In the case of conceptual knowledge this function is performed by using language as a means of actually conveying conceptual information from one person to another. Each word has a definite conceptual content represented by its dictionary definition. Sentences are already propositional in form, and their structure is naturally suited to the logical manipulation and transmission of conceptual information. In the case of non-conceptual knowledge, however, language can of course no longer be used in this way at all. Neither the conceptual content of words nor the rational structure of sentences is applicable to it. This kind of knowledge is ineffable and inexpressible so that it cannot be taught or conveyed to another.

In order to see how non-conceptual knowledge is dealt with in community we must turn to a very different function of which every natural language is capable and which has already been described briefly in the last chapter. The possibility of this new function arises out of the circumstance that many words possess numinous overtones beyond their purely conceptual content. By a sufficiently skillful use of such words in appropriate combinations and contexts, it is possible to use language in a way which arouses or evokes a specific numinous experience in the hearer or reader. In such use of language nothing tangible passes from one person to another. No conceptual information is conveyed because, of course, there is nothing substantive of a conceptual nature to be transmitted. Neither grammar and sentence structure nor the dictionary meaning of words are involved when language is used in this evocative manner. Nevertheless, all natural languages always have been, and continue to be, employed in this manner by human communities for the nurture, development, and mutual understanding and sharing of their non-conceptual knowledge. This is an empirical fact which is completely overlooked in modern attempts by logical positivists to overcome the supposed deficiencies of natural language by inventing a purely conceptual and logical artificial language. Such efforts are doomed to remain mere academic curiosities not because people in general are stubbornly opposed to innovations but simply because, having arbitrarily rejected at the outset the whole category of the non-conceptual, such artificial languages leave men powerless to cope with what is really a very essential component of their total knowledge.

We are now in a position to return to our example of the child and his knowledge of tigers and to see how his family is able to assist him in the development of the numinous component of this knowledge. A striking example of the use of language for just this purpose is provided by Blake's famous poem:

> Tyger, Tyger, burning bright
> In the forests of the night,
> What immortal hand or eye
> Could frame thy fearful symmetry?

Indeed the entire poem should be read in this connection. With it as guide and example, we can then readily imagine to ourselves how within the family circle the embryonic intuent of a tiger which had just begun to form in the child's mind could be filled out and evocatively built up over a long period of evolving experience. It would all be done through the use of language; in the telling of a story through the right choice of word or phrase, of hushed silence or startled exclamation, even of accompanying facial expression or gesture. Again it would be accomplished incidentally, too, when language was being used primarily to convey information and answer questions having to do with the concept of tiger. This would be done through a numinous surcharge accompanying the words and propositions employed for the clarification of conceptual knowledge. Indeed our simple Indian family would have no idea of the distinction we are attempting to elucidate here between conceptual and non-conceptual knowledge and experience. To them both the tiger and their knowledge of the tiger would be unitary. To them also their language would be simply the natural means they had for sharing and communicating with each other. Whenever employed, it would simultaneously convey conceptual information and evoke non-conceptual experience, with no consciously recognized distinction between them.

The distinction between the concept and the intuent of one and the same object is particularly clear and essential in the special case of a sacrament. There the concept, or "outward and visible sign," is clearly distinguished from "the inward and spiritual grace" which is the intuent of the sacrament. Having pointed this out, it may not be out of order to note that much confusion in sacramental theology is caused by the attempt to treat the non-conceptual component, the intuent, as though it were a concept subject to all rational categories of conceptual knowledge.

My purpose in all this has been twofold. First I have attempted to make manifest the existence of a true category of non-conceptual knowledge in parallel with the accepted category of conceptual or rational knowledge and to claim for the former a status as secure and honorable as that which we accord to the latter. Second, I have sought to sketch in the outlines of a non-conceptual epistemology in a way which would suggest the possibility of developing it as fully as has been done with the conceptual epistemologies which we already possess. Doubtless a much more detailed and careful treatment than that attempted here would be required for any degree of success in either objective. I trust, however, that enough may have been done to reveal at least a path for further inquiry and to indicate the potential fruitfulness of its pursuit.

Knowledge in Encounter

Let us now consider the second of the two additional modes of knowledge. In several respects this second mode represents a much more drastic departure from conventional epistemology than does the claim that a non-conceptual knowledge exists side by side with conceptual knowledge. The reason for this is that it rests on the introduction of an entirely different relationship between subject and object than that contemplated in conventional epistemology. This different order of relationship, although entirely familiar in ordinary human affairs at the sub-intellectual level, is nevertheless alien to the main stream of philosophic discourse. Even after I have described this mode of knowledge in some detail, and shown that in ordinary usage the term "knowledge" has always included it, to many it will still seem to put a strain on the term to include in it, on the same basis as, say, scientific knowledge, that knowledge which arises out of the new relationship. It is my conviction that such dubiousness reflects a shortcoming in contemporary thinking about the nature of knowledge more than it does a weakness in the case I shall make for defining that which is known in the new relationship as true knowledge. This, however, each reader will, of course, have to judge for himself when my case is complete. My reason for bringing up this expectation here at the outset is simply to warn the reader in advance that my interpretation of the verb "to know" is bound to seem radical.

For the discovery of this different order of relationship which adds a new dimension to the act of knowing, I am indebted to Martin Buber's remarkable little book, *I and Thou.* This book marks a major turning point in the whole course of western thought. It is an epoch-making book which, in the relatively short period since its publication in 1923, has already had a profound influence on both philosophy and theology quite out of proportion to its slender size. I have already made extensive use of it elsewhere* when discussing the ideas of freedom, destiny, and providence. Here my use of it will be confined to the problem of knowledge and to the question of what we can properly claim to know as well as the basis on which we can defend such claims.

Our entire consideration of the problem of knowledge up to this point has been exclusively within the context of what Buber calls the relationship of *I and It.* The locus of knowledge is the *I*, considered as a seat of consciousness and experience. This *I* is immersed in a world of objects and events—the *It*—which the *I* experiences and seeks to know and to understand. In both forms of knowledge which we have considered so far, the knower, which is the *I,* is separated from this world of *It* by a thin boundary layer of perception roughly coincident with his skin which is the outermost point of origin of all his experience. The total store of concepts and intuents with all their interrelationships which constitute the totality of his knowledge, in the sense in which we have been using the word, is inside this boundary layer in the *I*'s mind

* William G. Pollard, *Chance and Providence.* New York: Scribner's, 1958.

and consciousness. The entire external world which he knows is outside this boundary. This boundary forms an impenetrable barrier of separation which holds off the domain of the *I* from the domain of the *It*.

The new relationship which Buber unveils and reveals so clearly in his book, and which he designates as that of I and Thou, is something totally different from the *I-It* relationship. This new relationship is of a different dimension and cannot even be discussed in the same terms as is the *I-It* relationship just described. It does not investigate explicitly the line of boundary which separates the *I* from the *It* simply because the processes of perception and experience are not involved in it. You would never speak, for example, about one whom you love, with whom you have a relationship, in the same terms as those used of an *object* which you *experience*. The *I-Thou* relationship has a character which escapes comprehension when the usual categories of experiencing, feeling, perceiving, investigating, observing, and using are employed. And this is so not because the usual categories are rejected or denied; but rather because the relationship is so different in character and so incommensurate with the usual categories that there is simply no way in which they can be applied to it. What are needed instead are the categories of confrontation, encounter, and meeting; of commitment and sacrifice; of giving and receiving; of alienation, nostalgia, restlessness, adventure, presentness, and fulfillment. These categories do not exclude the others; they are simply totally different from them.

In order to begin the process of unveiling the new world of *I and Thou,* consider two perceiving subjects each of whom is the seat of a store of both conceptual and non-conceptual knowledge as we have defined these. Each one of them is enclosed within the boundary of his skin in such a way that everything he knows is "inside" him, and all the objects and events in the "outside" world, which make up the content of this knowledge, can affect him only through whatever influences originating from these objects and events may impinge on this boundary layer of perception. Each of these two centers of experiencing and knowing can experience, observe, and investigate the other as merely one more object among the manifold objects which people his external world. It is vitally important to see the force of this conclusion. In the context of all traditional epistemology, every other person in the whole world, every plant and animal, everything else which exists at all, even every spirit including God himself, is *necessarily* placed in the status of an object in the external world of the observer. Everything else besides oneself is unavoidably an *It*—a thing to be experienced, investigated, understood, and used. Even if there is such a thing as extra-sensory perception, it is just one more way of experiencing that which lies outside of the subject who experiences and knows. To strive for anything else in this subject-object context would require something far more drastic than extra-sensory perception. It would demand nothing less than a way to "get out of our skins" so that we would not have to experience at all in order to know.

This impasse into which we have been driven immediately raises the question as to whether there may not be some other relationship in which these two centers of experience and knowledge can stand with respect to each other, apart from that in which each one is necessarily reduced to the status of a mere object in the external world of the other? To this question there is a very simple, almost embarrassingly obvious answer. We can reply, "Yes! Why not let them simply *meet* each other?" Meeting is mutual. When two persons meet, each one has the same ontological status as the other. It is not that one is a subject and the other an object. Neither one is an object in the external world of the other to be experienced and used. A meeting is rather the confrontation of two pre-existent beings who face each other across the void and say "Thou" to each other. In this simple process of meeting, the new dimension of *I and Thou* is revealed. Do not think though that it involves something strange and mystical; a kind of vitalism or spiritualism perhaps. The danger is that our unfamiliarity with this new dimension, the fact that we have never heard anyone talk about or take it seriously before, will mask its essential simplicity and unadorned reality from us.

Some years ago a schoolmate gave my youngest son a baby mouse. It was a black laboratory mouse with pink tail and ears which had doubtless been passed on by a scientist or technician working in the Oak Ridge laboratories. My son was very excited about this mouse, so we bought a large, fancy cage for it with a feeding platform, water dispenser, and exercise wheel, and made the mouse a member of the family. We even named him Stewart Little and called him Stewart, for short. In time my son became quite familiar and easy with Stewart and often would take him out of his cage and play with him on a screened porch off the living room where there was no danger of losing him. He would let the mouse run up and down his arms and body, even up under his shirt sleeve and, of course, all around the porch and the furniture on it. Being interested in the mouse, my son naturally studied him intently with absorbing interest. You could see him examining in detail the mouse's eyes, whiskers, feet, and fur. His delicate, paper-thin ears and peculiar tail were objects of especial interest. His behavior, too, and his response to various stimuli were fascinating to observe. It was interesting to see him run and then suddenly stop, tensely alert and expectant. What would he do now if you did so-and-so to him? In all this and much more the mouse was an object in my son's external world. A very cute and interesting object, to be sure, and one which was a source of much pleasure, enjoyment, and satisfaction, but still an object to be studied, observed, experienced, and used. In all of this my son was gaining knowledge, doubtless not only rational but numinous knowledge as well, of the mouse. My son was the subject and Stewart his object. All of this, in other words, was taking place in the world of *I and It*.

Every now and then, however, while my son was playing with Stewart something different would take place. It might be when the mouse, having run down his arm, would stop still in the palm of his hand and look at him. For a moment then these two totally different beings, with no means whatever of communicating with each other, would simply face each other, confronting each other across the void. My son, who a moment before had been laughing with delight over the antics of the mouse, would in such a moment become very still and a profoundly solemn look would come over his face. For just a moment these two beings would stare at each other as though to say, "Who are you? What is the mystery of existence like for you? Do you care about me? Do you *know* me?" Such a moment would never last very long; one or the other would soon break it up and they would be playing again as before. But who can doubt that in that moment something very different from the subject-object relationship had occurred? These two creatures were meeting each other; two unique beings confronting each other across the void of non-being. In that moment neither one was experiencing, observing, enjoying, or fearing the other. Neither was merely the other's object. The new dimension of the *I and Thou* was revealed in it.

Buber has a wonderful passage along just this line of thought with respect to a tree. The tree as object can be experienced, studied, and understood in a variety of ways. But the tree as being, which exists in the same way and on the same basis as I exist, can also simply confront me. It is worth quoting the passage in full:

> I consider a tree.
>
> I can look on it as a picture: stiff column in a shock of light, or splash of green shot with the delicate blue and silver of the background.
>
> I can perceive it as movement: flowing veins on clinging, pressing pith, suck of the roots, breathing of the leaves, ceaseless commerce with earth and air—and the obscure growth itself.
>
> I can classify it in a species and study it as a type in its structure and mode of life.
>
> I can subdue its actual presence and form so sternly that I recognize it only as an expression of law—of the laws in accordance with which a constant opposition of forces is continually adjusted, or of those in accordance with which the component substances mingle and separate.
>
> I can dissipate it and perpetuate it in number, in pure numerical relation.
>
> In all this the tree remains my object, occupies space and time, and has its nature and constitution.

It can, however, also come about, if I have both will and grace, that in considering the tree I become bound up in relation to it. The tree is now no longer *It*. I have been seized by the power of exclusiveness.

To effect this it is not necessary for me to give up any of the ways in which I consider the tree. There is nothing from which I would have to turn my eyes away in order to see, and no knowledge that I would have to forget. Rather is everything, picture and movement, species and type, law and number, indivisibly united in this event.

Everything belonging to the tree is in this: its form and structure, its colours and chemical composition, its intercourse with the elements and with the stars, are all present in a single whole.

The tree is no impression, no play of my imagination, no value depending on my mood; but it is bodied over against me and has to do with me, as I with it—only in a different way.

Let no attempt be made to sap the strength from the meaning of the relation: relation is mutual.

The tree will have a consciousness, then, similar to our own? Of that I have no experience. But do you wish, through seeming to succeed in it with yourself, once again to disintegrate that which cannot be disintegrated? I encounter no soul or dryad of the tree, but the tree itself. (pp. 7-8)

One would have to read all of Buber's little book over and over, and then besides produce many other concrete examples from one's own experience, before the real solidarity and simple reality of the world of *I and Thou* could really emerge and become apparent. In order to be able to get on with the main question of the character of knowledge, we shall, unfortunately, have to be content here with only a few additional observations and then a summary in Buber's own words. The first of these observations is a word of caution which I have found it necessary to emphasize in discussing this subject. Sometimes there is a tendency among those to whom the existence of the world of *I and Thou* has first been revealed to embrace it with such enthusiasm as to wish to reject the more familiar world of *I and It* as being somehow unworthy and ignoble. Against this tendency it is necessary to point out emphatically that the former is really *impossible* without the latter. It is obviously impossible to say *Thou* to any being which cannot in any way be experienced and so be made an object of one's external world. This is true even of God. If there were no such thing as the experience of the holy, no hint even of the mysterium tremendum, then the very idea of God would simply never have occurred. There must be some kind of experiential basis for the existence of another being before it is possible to enter into relationship with that being. Moreover, the *I-Thou* relationship is always essentially momentary and fleeting, and always dissolves back again into the *I-It* relationship. The very ground and basis of marriage is an *I-Thou* relationship between husband and wife expressing the bond of love and devotion between them and constituting certainly the major source of the knowledge they have of each other. Yet even there during most of the time that they are together, each one is observing and perceiving the other, recognizing the other's physical and psychological features, behavior patterns, fancies, and foibles. At such times each one occupies the status of an object in the external world of the other. This is true even of our relationship with God. It is only in worship, or occasionally elsewhere, as when in association with others we are gripped by the power of the Holy Spirit in community, that we are in the primary *I-Thou* relationship with him. At other times in our reflective moments even he must become an *It* for us, that is, an object in our external world to be inquired about and, to whatever extent may be possible, understood. Moreover, it is entirely proper that this should be the case. For, otherwise, we would have to say that the whole of theology was improper, since in theological inquiry God is always an object for investigation and understanding. Let us not suppose, therefore, that there is any way of doing away with the world of *I and It*.

The reverse, however, is not true. There is no corresponding ingrained necessity for the appearance of the world of *I and Thou*. As Buber expresses it, every "particular *Thou*, after the relational event has run its course, *is bound* to become an *It*," while on the other hand every "particular *It*, by entering the relational event, *may* become a *Thou*." It is possible, though not very frequent, for a human being to so desire a completely autonomous existence with no entangling relationships with other beings as to approximate a condition in which for him there is only one *I* with everything else which exists simply an object in the external world which that *I* experiences and uses. An example is to be found in Sartre, who feels that he can only be human if left alone and would lose himself if interfered with. Yet it is the source of Sartre's terrible despair that he recognizes more keenly than most the fundamental absurdity and unreality of the autonomous self which draws nothing from anyone or anything outside it; which only experiences and uses a given world without itself needing anything. Another example is Eric Hoffer, who both in his own life and in his book *The True Believer*, strives toward the ideal of the completely autonomous existence. An object of our experience has the opportunity, but not the necessity, of presenting itself to us as another being provided there is both the will and the grace for the necessary meeting.

When one places oneself as the perceiving and knowing subject over against an experienced world of things and events which is to be observed without involvement and subjected to the power of one's understanding, one has the essence of the world of *I and It*. This is, of course, also the world which is the exclusive concern of the subject matter of all science. The character of this world is summed up by Buber in the following passage:

> [Man] perceives what exists around about him—simply things, and beings as things; and what happens round about him—simply events, and actions as events; things consisting of qualities, events of moments; things entered in the graph of place, events in that of time; things and events bounded by other things and events, measured by them, comparable with them: he perceives an ordered and detached world. It is to some extent a reliable world, having density and duration. Its organisation can be surveyed and brought out again and again; gone over with closed eyes, and verified with open eyes. It is always there, next to your skin, if you look on it that way, cowering in your soul, if you prefer it so. It is your object, remains it as long as you wish, and remains a total stranger, within you and without. You perceive it, take it to yourself as the 'truth,' and it lets itself be taken; but it does not give itself to you. Only concerning it

may you make yourself 'understood' with others; it is ready, though attached to everyone in a different way, to be an object common to you all. But you cannot meet others in it. You cannot hold on to life without it, its reliability sustains you; but should you die in it, your grave would be in nothingness. (pp. 31-32)

In contrast to this world Buber describes the fundamental characteristics of the world of *I and Thou* in the following passage:

On the other hand, man meets what exists. . . . These meetings are not organised to make the world, but each is a sign of the world-order. They are not linked up with one another, but each assures you of your solidarity with the world. The world which appears to you in this way is unreliable, for it takes on a continually new appearance; you cannot hold it to its word. It has no density, for everything in it penetrates everything else; no duration, for it comes even when it is not summoned, and vanishes even when it is tightly held. It cannot be surveyed, and if you wish to make it capable of survey you lose it. . . . Between you and it there is mutual giving: you say *Thou* to it and give yourself to it, it says *Thou* to you and gives itself to you. You cannot make yourself understood with others concerning it, you are alone with it. But it teaches you to meet others, and to hold your ground when you meet them. Through the graciousness of its comings and the solemn sadness of its goings it leads you away to the *Thou* in which the parallel lines of relations meet. It does not help to sustain you in life, it only helps you to glimpse eternity. (pp. 32-33)

Assuming that the reality, as well as the universality, of the world of *I and Thou* has now been described and delineated with sufficient clarity, let us turn to the question of knowledge as it applies to this new dimension. To begin with, it will be well to look simply empirically at the question first, rather than philosophically or speculatively. For this purpose we need only ask whether in fact men in various cultures and epochs have commonly spoken of that which came to them out of confrontation and meeting as knowledge. As one piece of evidence of this we may cite the common and prevalent use of the verb "to know" in the question, "Do you know John Smith?", and its use in such replies as, "Oh, yes. I know him very well," or "I know him only slightly, since we have just met." Obviously the kind of "knowing" to which reference is made in the question and replies cited is very different from the kind of "knowing" implied in the question, "Do you know the color of John Smith's eyes?" In several languages this difference is emphasized by the use of different words to describe these two forms of knowledge, as with *kennen* and *wissen* in German and *connaître* and *savoir* in French. Yet, significantly the English language employs the same word to describe both. Apparently, wholly apart from any theoretical considerations about the nature or basis of knowledge, common usage in English recognizes a close and intimate kinship between the insights and understandings which come through encounter and meeting, and those which come through experience and rationalization.

The knowledge which comes through encounter and meeting is radically different in quality from conceptual knowledge which comes through observation and reason. For one thing it is much more immediate, vivid, and living. It is not organized in a complex, interconnected system as conceptual knowledge is. Such knowledge, for all its rational coherence and beauty of intricate detail, must be thought of piece by piece and cannot be apprehended all at once. The knowledge of encounter, on the other hand, is based on the memory of previous meetings, and that which is known, when called back by memory, becomes present again as a single whole.

To know John Smith, as a physiologist or biochemist would know him, involves a vast amount of factual information of the most intricate and detailed sort. No one individual can have all of this information, as it is presently known, stored in his mind. Even a highly trained specialist who has a great deal of it in his mind, cannot consciously know at any instant more than a minute portion of it. As he uses this knowledge, he simply calls up out of the recesses of his mind that bit of it which he needs at the moment. He realizes that this vast assortment of information is really organized into a beautifully structured, integrated whole. Yet he has never been able to have a vision of this complete whole in a single flash of the imagination. All he can possibly do is to assure himself that it is there by going over it again and again in his mind and verifying its coherence and logical structure at every step. This is the way with all systematic conceptual knowledge, and that, of course, includes all scientific knowledge.

To know John Smith, as his wife would say that she knows him, is, on the other hand, something very different. The best we can do to describe it is to say that her knowledge is *personal* knowledge. When he is absent from her and she wishes to make use of this knowledge of him, she needs only to call him to mind, and in a flash he is there in her imagination in person, that is, as a single whole being. The process by which this is accomplished in her mind is simply that of recalling in memory a meeting with him. She needs only to *confront* him in imagination and he is present to her in the whole of his being. It is just such a presentment of her husband that she will have in mind when she speaks of her knowledge of him. Yet this knowledge does not in any way exclude the other form. She of course also knows in addition a great deal *about* him—the color of his eyes and hair, his likes and dislikes, his peculiarities and deficiencies, and his strengths and weaknesses. If you pressed her, she would speak of all this, too, as her knowledge of her husband, gained over many years of close observation and intimate experience.

This twofold character of knowledge arises out of the twofold character of reality wherein the knower, the *I,* may either become bound up in relationship with another being as his *Thou,* or merely experience the same being as his object, his *It.* Philosophical theories of knowledge have generally rejected the former mode and confined the use of the word "knowledge" exclusively to the rational and conceptual form of the latter. Common usage continues, however, to speak of both modes as knowledge, and, if anything, reverses philosophy by giving precedence to the former. Indeed, we would come close to the spirit of this common usage if we restricted the idea of *knowing* to that form of knowledge which comes through confrontation and meeting only, and spoke of that which comes through experience and observation as *understanding* rather than knowing. The meaning and value of such a usage was brought home to me with particular force through a quotation from Lionel Trilling's *The Liberal Imagination* which is quoted in his chapter on encounter by J. H. Oldham in his excellent book *Life Is Commitment:*

> There is something repulsive in the idea of men being studied for their own good. The paradigm of what repels us is to be found in the common situation of the child who is *understood* by its parents, hemmed in, anticipated and lovingly circumscribed, thoroughly typed, finding it easier and easier to conform internally and in the future to the parent's own interpretation of the external acts of the past, and so, yielding to understanding as never to coercion, does not develop the mystery and wildness of spirit which it is still our grace to believe is the mark of full humanism. The act of understanding is an act of control. (page 31)

After reading this passage it is well to reflect on its implications for a restrictive theory of knowledge such as that maintained in logical positivism. In such a theory the only real knowledge we could have at all of our children would be an understanding of them. To know them in the way we would wish to know them would be excluded as meaningless.

The kind of knowledge we are speaking of here, which comes to us out of our entry into the world of *I and Thou* and which we acquire through meeting, encounter, sacrifice, and grace, is just the kind which is almost always meant when the Bible uses the words "know" or "knowledge." Once the distinction between knowledge in the sense of understanding and knowledge in its existential sense has become firmly established in one's mind, it is illuminating as one reads the Bible to note in each passage where the word "know" occurs in which of these two senses it is being used. Knowledge which is acquired by a dispassionate observer rationally perfecting his conceptual experience of objects and events—that is, knowledge in the sense in which it is understood in epistemology—is almost totally absent from Biblical usage. The dominating Biblical aim is always to know the objects of experience as entities or beings, to know face to face, so to speak. The correlative aim of knowing *about* such objects, in the sense of accumulating systematic information about them so as to understand their role and function within a rationally integrated conceptual framework, is almost totally absent from the Bible. One of the most dramatic symbols of what is meant by knowledge in the Biblical sense is the distinctive Old Testament usage of "know" for the act of sexual intercourse, as in the recurring phrase, "And ________ knew his wife ________, and she conceived and bore ________," or in the account of David's old age in the opening portion of I Kings where it says, "The maiden was very beautiful; and she became the king's nurse and ministered to him; but the king knew her not." The encounter of person to person acquires a depth and vividness through the sacramental power and profound intimacy of the sexual act which is unequalled in any other human relationship. By speaking of the performance of the act itself as "knowing," the Bible uniquely illuminates what it intends to have recognized as a primary quality of the whole category of knowledge.

Summary

In order to summarize what I have been attempting to do in this chapter, I should like to make use of a diagram of the epistemological problem for which I am indebted to my friend, Professor Henry Margenau of Yale University, and which he has employed extensively for the clarification of the nature of scientific knowledge. His diagram I would make the first of three separate diagrams, or else the first stage in a threefold development of a complete diagram representing all forms of knowledge. This first stage, Figure 1, I label "Conceptual Knowledge from Experience." Following Margenau's schemata we draw first a vertical line and label it the "P-plane." This line represents the plane of perception, the boundary between subject and object, between knowledge and reality. Everything to the right of this

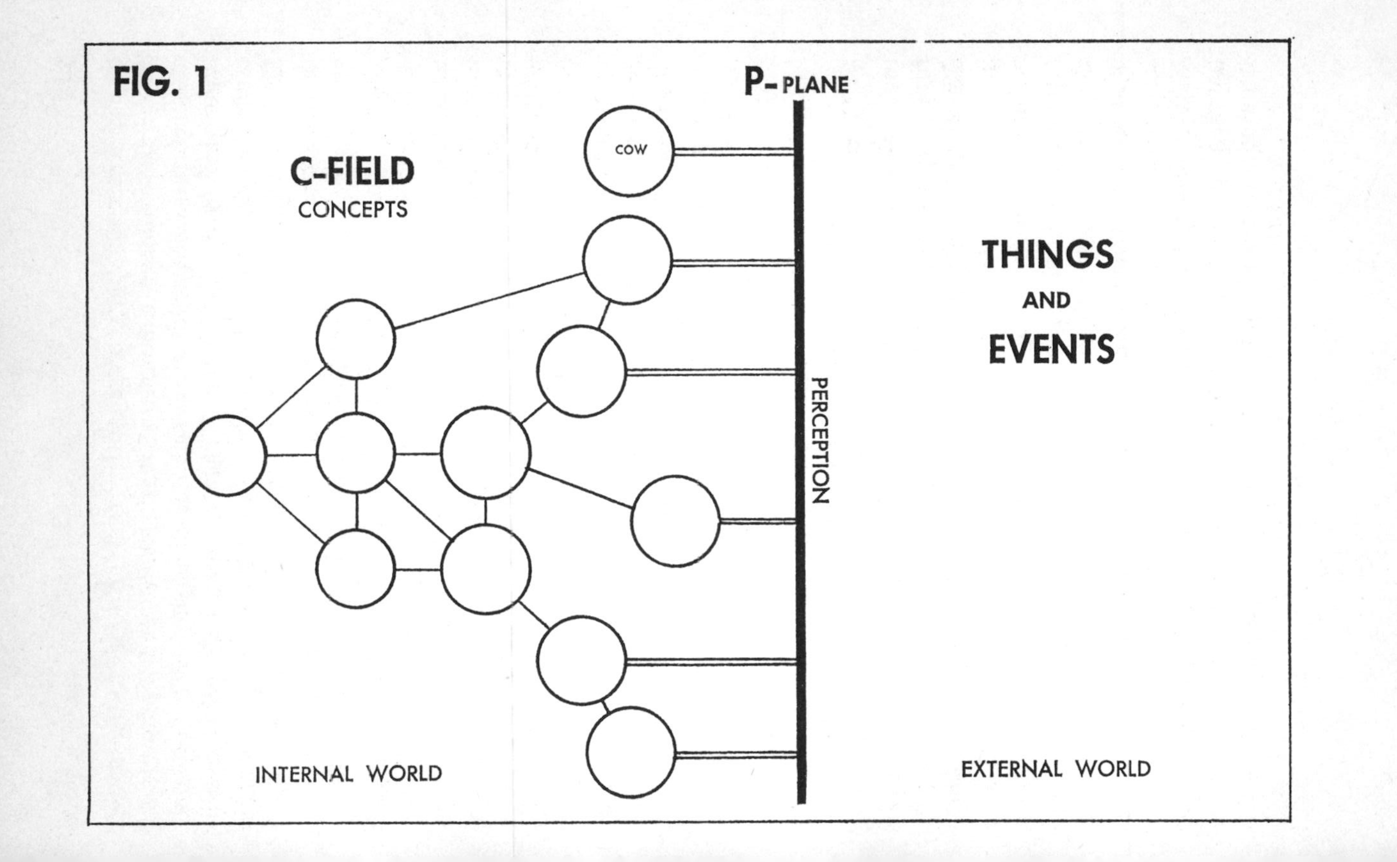
FIG. 1
C-FIELD
CONCEPTS
COW
P-PLANE
PERCEPTION
THINGS
AND
EVENTS
INTERNAL WORLD
EXTERNAL WORLD

line is "external" and represents that which belongs to the outside world. Everything to the left of it is "inside" and represents the store of rational knowledge which the observer has in his mind. Somewhat to the left of the P-plane we place a vertical row of circles to represent concepts, or as Margenau designates them for the greater precision required in science, "constructs." Each of these circles are labeled as a particular concept or construct, and has one or more lines drawn from it terminating at the vertical line of the P-plane, which represent what Margenau calls "rules of correspondence" because they define the particular ways in which concepts are related to and connected with direct or immediate experience. Further to the left other circles are drawn to represent concepts or constructs of a first order of abstraction which are related to other more primitive concepts in the mind, but not themselves related directly to experience. These interrelationships among concepts are represented in the diagram by lines connecting the various circles with each other. These lines represent the logical propositions and mathematical laws which systematize our conceptual knowledge of the world and make possible the coherent rational organization of knowledge achieved in the sciences. All of these lines and circles make up what Margenau calls the C-field, the field of concepts.

To this basic diagram of Margenau's representing the nature and structure of conceptual knowledge, I add a second stage of my own in Figure 2 which I label "Non-conceptual Knowledge from Experience." This diagram is constructed by drawing inside some of the first row of circles, representing concepts directly derived from experience, an inner dotted circle to represent a non-conceptual overtone, or "intuent," associated with the concept in question. I also draw one or two dotted circles by themselves to represent intuents, like God or Spirit, not associated with an immediately perceived concept, but having a small inner solid-line circle inscribed within them to represent a small auxiliary conceptual content in such intuents. These dotted circles are then also connected by dotted lines to the P-plane to indicate the modes of correspondence in the mind between the intuent and

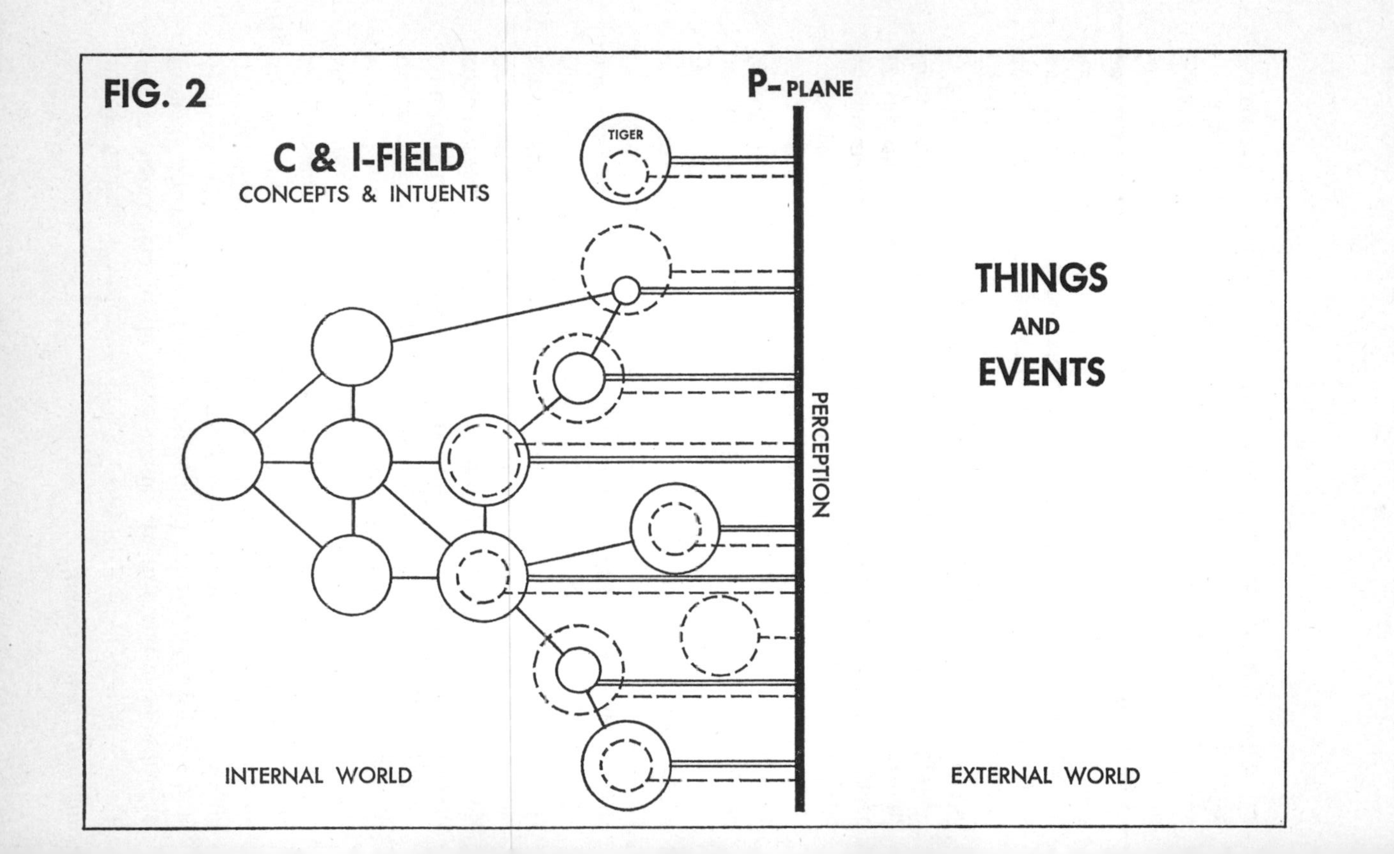
FIG. 2
C & I-FIELD
CONCEPTS & INTUENTS
TIGER
P- PLANE
PERCEPTION
THINGS
AND
EVENTS
INTERNAL WORLD
EXTERNAL WORLD

the numinous experience out of which it was derived, which of course also originates in the P-plane. In this way it is seen that intuents emerge out of, and correspond to, numinous experience in much the same way that concepts emerge out of and correspond to rational experience. There are, however, no dotted lines connecting these intuent circles with each other, and no dotted circles among the full concept circles far to the left which represent concepts derived by rational abstraction from other concepts. The absence of such dotted connecting lines corresponds to our inability to rationalize, manipulate, or systematize our nonconceptual knowledge which, because we are not even able to conceive it, cannot be propositionally related in any way but can only be evoked. Having completed this second stage of the diagram of knowledge, I would assert that the dotted structure is just as real and just as firmly grounded in experience as the solid-line structure, and that no really defensible argument exists for the a priori elimination of one and retention of the other. I would assert that each has an equally authentic claim to be called knowledge.

The third and final stage in the development of my diagram of knowledge is shown in Figure 3 and is labeled simply "Knowledge from Encounter." In order to exhibit it in diagram form, it is necessary to draw two vertical "P-plane" lines in the middle of the figure to represent now two pre-existent beings in place of the one observer before. To represent the fact that each of these beings *also* possesses the equipment for experiential knowledge, I have drawn to the left of the P-plane on the left and to the right of the P-plane on the right a duplicate set of solid-line and dotted circles with appropriate connecting solid or dotted lines exactly as in the second stage of the diagram. These represent the fact that each of these two experiencing and knowing beings can be an object in the external world of the other, namely, an *It* for the other, capable of being experienced, observed, and studied through isolated intuents and systematized concepts.

The most important difference which I need to emphasize between this diagram and the others has to do with what the

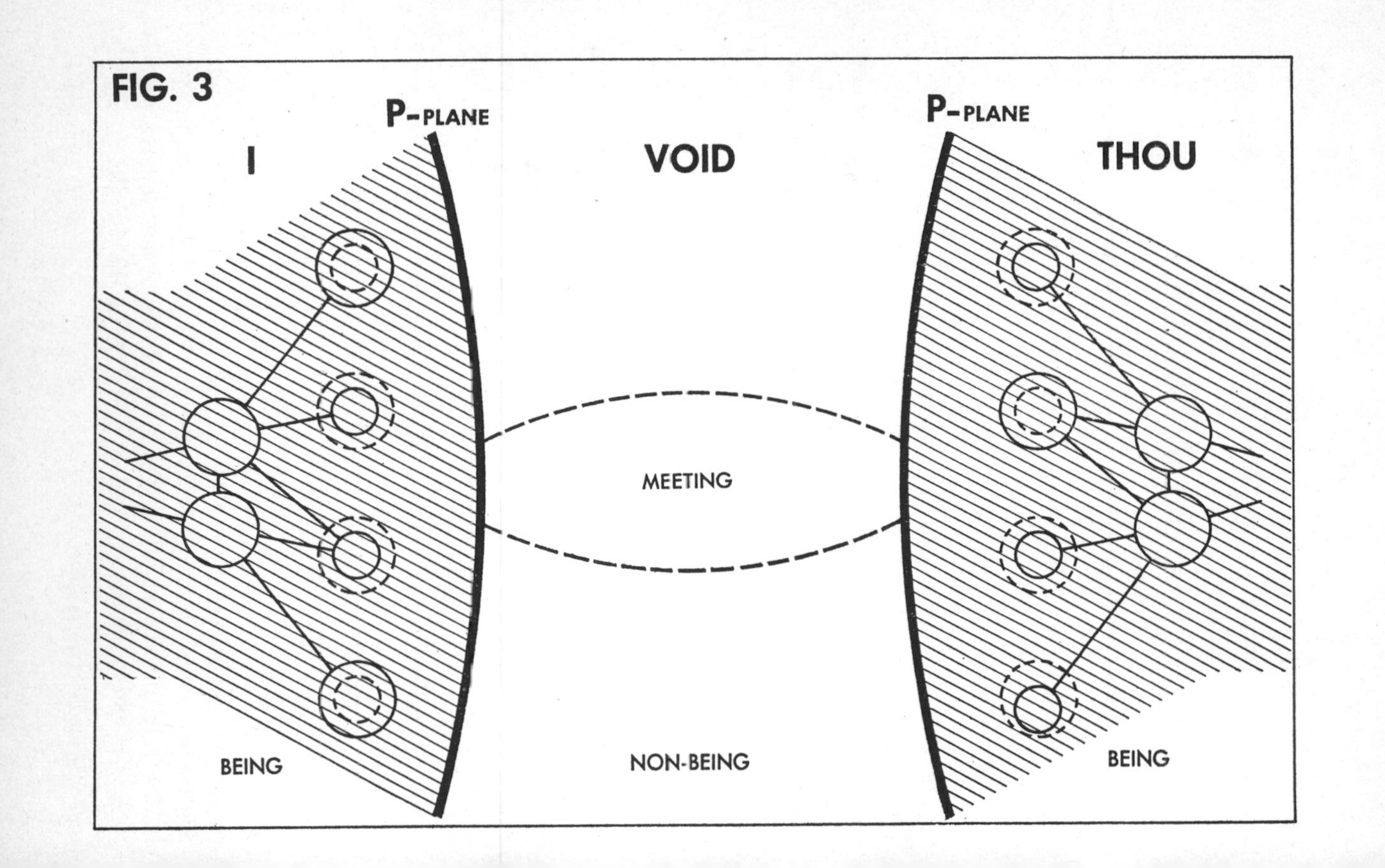
FIG. 3
P-PLANE
P-PLANE
I
VOID
THOU
MEETING
BEING
NON-BEING
BEING

space in the middle, between the two vertical P-plane lines, represents. For in order to exhibit the possibility of the kind of knowledge to be represented by this diagram, it is essential to realize that this space can no longer be taken to represent the external world, peopled with objects and events, of either of the two perceiving subjects. Rather it must now be taken to stand for and represent the void which separates each circumscribed finite being from every other. The space between is now really empty and simply separates two distinct, bounded, and separable beings, the one diagrammed at the left and the other diagrammed at the right, whose meeting across the void of non-being between them is thereby made possible. If one were to imagine the space between to be cluttered with things and events, there would be introduced so overpowering a distraction that the two beings would be isolated from each other and unable to meet. If you wish to meet another, you must abandon during the moment of meeting your own external world so that there is nothing left between you but the void which sets off your being from his.

In order to complete this diagram we have now only to draw two symmetrically placed bowed, dashed lines above and below the axis of the diagram to represent the mutuality of the meeting, the encounter, or the bond of relationship which has taken place. These lines represent not only the meeting itself, but also the knowledge which each being has of the other as a result of the meeting. Unlike the experiential knowledge represented by concepts and intuents which each one has inside him in his isolation, this knowledge must always be between them because of the essential mutuality of relationship. One sees this in the fact that after the meeting has taken place and the two beings are again separated from each other, the only way either one can have this knowledge of the other, in the sense of really exercising it, is by actually resurrecting in memory and imagination the meeting itself. In this act the other being is again known to you, not as your object with attributes and characteristics, but in person in the unity and wholeness of his being. Having completed this last diagram I would assert of it too that it represents true knowledge and that no purely theoretical or philosophic argument designed to eliminate it, however cleverly devised, can overcome the weight of the universal witness of mankind that in just this process is to be found the highest, the truest, and the most vivid of all forms of knowledge which men possess.

These three diagrams provide what it seems to me might become the skeleton or framework around which could be developed a complete epistemology or theory of knowledge which could overcome many of the obvious omissions, deficiencies, and inadequacies of traditional treatments of the subject, and restore to it the advantage of a one-to-one correspondence between elements of the theory and the actual living experience of mankind. It seems possible in this way to have ultimately an epistemology in which all of the various ways in which men in all cultures and at all times have claimed to have knowledge would find their proper place and setting. How much better and more complete and proper such a theory would be than those contemporary versions which solve the problem by simply throwing out and rejecting as unreal, invalid, and meaningless such vast portions of what men have always claimed that they knew just as surely and securely as they did the rational segment of their knowledge.

VI

The Problem of Revelation

AMONG THE problems which beset the relationship between science and Christianity, none seems to present difficulties of a more fundamentally irreconcilable nature than the claim of the Church to possess a store of valid and authentic knowledge given by revelation. To the scientifically trained mind, the very idea of the possibility of a revealed form of knowledge is likely to prove anathema. Scientific knowledge unfolds slowly through the painstaking efforts of many individuals in the scientific community. It is gained only through long and sustained labor of the most demanding sort, and involves for each person engaged in the enterprise great personal discipline and often many frustrations and disappointments. To the scientist it seems somehow profoundly right and proper that it should be this way, and that each new piece of knowledge should be all the more treasured and rejoiced over because it was so hard won. Against this background of the preciousness of knowledge as it is gained bit by bit in science, the idea of knowledge coming by a different route as information simply revealed without striving or effort is unpalatable. To one who has known the sense of real achievement which accompanies the gaining of each new understanding and insight in science, the idea of revealed knowledge is likely to seem on a par with copying answers out of an answer book at an examination.

This rather prevalent reaction to the idea of revealed knowledge among scientific people, and others influenced by them, is largely the result of a too narrow and restricted understanding of what is meant by knowledge. In the view of knowledge represented by logical positivism, nothing can properly be said to be known which is not discoverable by the methods of the natural sciences. This view effectively restricts knowledge to that particular form which, in the last chapter, we designated as conceptual knowledge from experience. If it were true that the knowledge given by revelation were of that kind, then the objection just outlined would doubtless have considerable merit. Revelation would then necessarily involve a by-passing and short-circuiting of the laborious and disciplined process of acquiring knowledge through investigation, rational inquiry, and empirical verification. There are, however, as we saw, other distinctly different ways of knowing than the one pursued by science. What we shall endeavor to show here is that revelation in its Biblical sense involves one of these other forms of knowledge, and that everything made known through it is of such a character that it could not, in any event, be discovered by the methods of science. It is, therefore, not an alternative route to knowledge in the scientific sense of the word, but rather represents an access to a form of knowledge which could not be had in any other way. Moreover, as we shall see, it is a kind of knowledge which emerges slowly and even painfully out of the life and history of a committed community and demands, of those belonging to that community, just as much self-discipline and commitment, as well as frustration and disappointment, as does the enterprise of science from those belonging to the scientific community. When revealed knowledge is properly understood, not only this primary objection, but many others as well which have been raised in the name of science, no longer hold.

There are three aspects of revelation in its Biblical sense which seem to me of primary importance and essential for an understanding of it. The first of these is that revelation arises exclusively out of the kind of knowledge which we have called "knowledge from encounter." Revelation, in other words, is a process which always takes place in the world of *I and Thou,* never in the world of *I and It.* The second essential aspect is that revelation, like spirit, is a corporate phenomenon which takes place in community rather than with individuals in isolation from community. The third point concerns the role of spirit in the inspiration required for gaining and expressing knowledge. In the discussion of the problem of revelation which follows, we shall take up these three aspects in the order just given.

Revelation as Divine-Human Encounter

For all peoples the basis and origin of a knowledge of God is to be found in numinous experience. Israel in this respect is no exception. The knowledge of the divine gained from such experience is not, however, a revelation. Rather as with all knowledge gained through direct perception and experience, whether conceptual or non-conceptual, it is referred to as acquired or discovered knowledge. Through it the reality, the existence, and the living presence of God becomes known, but not his person and nature. He is known only inexpressibly and ineffably as the *mysterium tremendum,* the *deus absconditus,* the God hidden in mystery and terrible in his majesty. This represents a true and authentic knowledge of God, just as authentic indeed as is any of our conceptual knowledge of created things. Moreover it is a kind of knowledge which essentially all human cultures have possessed. It is nearly as universal and non-particular as our conceptual knowledge of the world. Yet when compared to God as he is known in Christianity, it is an extremely inadequate and incomplete knowledge of him. It represents all that can be known of God apart from his revelation of himself. Revealed knowledge is, therefore, of a different character from this knowledge which comes out of man's experience of the numinous.

Revelation is a category of knowledge which belongs peculiarly to the world of *I and Thou*. Indeed, if we ask ourselves how it can be that any knowledge at all can be gained from the meeting or encounter of two beings, we shall have to conclude that this is only possible to the extent that each reveals himself to the other during the meeting. When we study or observe another person, then that other person is always only our object. The result of such observation is always knowledge *about* the other person, never knowledge *of* him. In that case we speak of discovering, acquiring, confirming, and verifying the knowledge we obtain. But when we meet or encounter another, then the other person is always another being with the same status in existence as ours, and whatever knowledge is gained from the encounter is always knowledge *of* him, never knowledge *about* him. In that case we naturally speak of the extent to which either party to the meeting conceals or reveals himself. Those who object to the possibility of revealed knowledge simply fail to see this distinction. There is no threat here to the security and autonomy of scientific knowledge. Information about the world and systematic knowledge of its structure and behavior must continue to be had by the painstaking methods of science. There is no threat that it ever has been, or ever will be, simply told to someone in a mystical trance so that all he has to do is write it down. Revelation is something very different from this and has, indeed, nothing to do with conveying information or systematic understanding.

Grave risks are involved in every real encounter, and it always takes courage to really meet another. In any ordinary meeting what one usually desires is to preserve the autonomy of his own self as the center of experience and knowledge, and to avoid meeting the other as a confronting being. The tendency, however, of that other, usually so successfully restrained to the status of an *object* in one's external world, to rise up out of the depths and to emerge and confront one is always a threat to the uniqueness and autonomy of one's own selfhood. One's immediate or spontaneous reaction to this threat is the desire to run away, to hide, to conceal one's self. It is only the realization that in this way lies complete isolation and death in the midst of the impersonal vastness of an alien universe that gives one the courage to turn and meet the other. The terrible risk is always there that during the meeting, as the relationship deepens, what develops will be a failure, a repudiation of one by the other. The only way the meeting can take place is for each to banish his shyness and throw himself recklessly into it, willfully and purposefully losing himself by sacrificing the secure and comfortable autonomy of the lone *I* which only experiences, enjoys, and uses an objective world of things and events. The frightful possibility that, after sacrificing so much, the meeting might end in concealment and rejection fills the anticipation of it with the dread of losing oneself, or a part of oneself. On the other hand, nothing can compare with the lovely excitement, joy, and wonder of the discovery of true graciousness in the other as the relationship deepens. This is revelation, and there is nothing merely automatic or mechanical about it. Revelation always comes by grace, and because the risk is so great and there is so much at stake, the recipient of grace is always amazed at finding it and relieved and overjoyed beyond measure with the gift of it.

Just as in the case of the knowledge which finite beings reveal to each other when they meet each other, so too all the knowledge of God which mankind possesses has been revealed in divine-human encounters. This is true not only of Judaism and Christianity, but of all religions which make any claim at all to a knowledge either of God or of gods. Throughout the history of mankind, various individuals have claimed to be the recipients of direct revelations from God. If one examines the reports they give of these revelatory events, one sees that the key element in them is always such an encounter. Not only for them but for all of their associates as well, God had already been experienced as the *mysterium tremendum,* so that the existence of him who might conceivably be met was already known by all and shared in common. Yet the risk of a total loss of self in a real meeting of mutuality with a Being of such infinite majesty is terrible, beyond comparison with the dread of meetings between finite created beings. This is what the author of Hebrews means when he says, "It is a terrible thing to fall into the hands of the living God." So for the most part God remains hidden to men behind the mystery of the inexpressible and non-conceptual object of numinous experience. But in the relatively rare cases in which the claim is made that God has revealed himself to a man, what has always happened, over and above this, is that some man has had a real encounter and meeting with, no longer just an experience of, the *mysterium tremendum.* This is what Archbishop Temple meant when he said in *Nature, Man and God*: "What is offered to man's apprehension in any specific revelation is not truth concerning God, but the living God himself." (page 322)

He who really meets God, face to face as it were, can only speak after the event, and then by analogy with human meetings, as though God had spoken to him. And indeed the assertion that knowledge of the Other is revealed in such a meeting must represent an interpersonal communication at the deepest level for which, in terms of language, no other description can be found. The Word of the Lord is indeed spoken in such a meeting, and he to whom it has been spoken can do none else but proclaim it thereafter. Yet when God speaks to man in this way, it is never so as to convey a previously unknown systematic knowledge of the world, or some new conceptual information about its order and structure. The individual emerges from the meeting with the same notions about the things and events in the world of his perceptual experience as he had already acquired from birth in his own particular cultural context, for the purpose and function of such a meeting is to come to know the living God himself, and not to pick up miscellaneous information. On the other hand, it always happens that such a person emerges from this meeting with a totally different outlook on the world. The status in creation which his fellow men take for granted for themselves, their self-centered motivations and desires, and their ideas of what life requires of them will now seem to him wholly incongruous, unreal, and tragically misguided. Knowing from this meeting the person of God and the vivid reality and burning actuality of his presence, the individual can only respond to the incongruities of the world after his encounter with God, by pronouncing to his fellow men, in the name of the true God, what God requires of them. Such pronouncements will, of course, be propositional in form and content and will represent the result of mental operations and rational processes as do other forms of knowledge in which an understanding of the objective world is sought. Moreover, in making these pronouncements, he can quite properly and with complete confidence claim that they represent divine revelations which he received directly from God. We must not, however, allow the validity of such a claim to mislead us into supposing that the propositional statements as such are directly transmitted in the process of revelation. They arise only after the revelation itself has taken place and when the mind reflects on the consequences of that which has become known in the meeting.

With this understanding of the nature of "revealed," as opposed to "acquired," knowledge, let us now turn to the question of the uniqueness of the Biblical revelation. This, as I shall attempt to show, depends almost entirely for its resolution on the role of community in the process of revelation. To put this question in a proper setting, I would first like to suggest that the revelation to Moses or Isaiah was not any different in its essential character, or even of a higher validity as a confrontation of the living God, than that, say, of Zoroaster or Mohammet. Certainly it would be contrary to all that we now know of God through the Biblical revelation itself, to suggest that these latter had really encountered a different being than the former. Unless one would wish to hold that the occasions of meeting which came to them with revelatory power were not really divine-human encounters at all, we must believe that the living God whom Zoroaster and Mohammet encountered was the one and only true God, and therefore the very same God who has made himself known through Israel. Moreover, there is nothing to suggest in any of the evidence available to us that the divine encounters to which non-Biblical religious figures bear witness as the source of their revelations were any different in their basic nature than those encounters experienced by the Biblical figures. On a purely individualistic basis, and apart from the context of the people and their history—that is, confining ourselves to the isolated individual and his encounter—there does not seem to be any proper ground on which to establish a claim for the uniqueness of one revelation over another.

Revelation in Community

What makes Israel, and the Bible which Israel produced, really unique and without parallel in all human history is the crucial and essential role played by community in achieving the knowledge of God. Unlike other peoples, the knowledge of the living God which was Israel's was not derived from any one religious leader. Even Moses, for all the central importance which he certainly has in Judaism, was one among many in the long history of Biblical revelation. He was born into a people who long before had come to know God in a way which set them apart from other peoples, and everything that he did and said was done and said as one of them. From their earliest roots in prehistory this people had known God in a way which none of the other peoples with whom they came in contact could claim to have known him. From the very beginning it had been a corporate experience, known and shared in and through community. As time went on and the events of their unfolding history made more and more strikingly evident to them the providential presence and activity of God in that history, they came to sense ever more clearly the uniqueness of their relationship to him. They came to realize explicitly that it was their special destiny as a people, the one single identifiable purpose of their whole corporate and historic existence, to know God and to reveal him to all the world: "To be a light to lighten the gentiles."

It took Israel many centuries of history, and extensive and varied contacts with other peoples, to become fully conscious of this special destiny and unique status. Perhaps it was not until the time of first Isaiah that this became really manifest. At any rate, in the movement of religious reform which came after him, it was made explicit as the following passages from Deuteronomy show very clearly:

For what great nation is there that has a god so near to it as the Lord our God is to us, whenever we call upon him?" (4:7). "For ask now of the days that are past, which were before you, since the day that God created man upon the earth, and ask from one end of heaven to the other, whether such a great thing as this has ever happened or was ever heard of. Did any people ever hear the voice of a god speaking out of the midst of the fire, as you have heard, and still live? Or has any god ever attempted to go and take a nation for himself from the midst of another nation, by trials, by signs, by wonders, and by war, by a mighty hand and an outstretched arm, and by great terrors, according to all that the Lord your God did for you in Egypt before your eyes? (4:32-34).

For you are a people holy to the Lord your God; the Lord your God has chosen you to be a people for his own possession, out of all the peoples that are on the face of the earth. It was not because you were more in number than any other people that the Lord set his love upon you and chose you, for you were the fewest of all peoples; but it is because the Lord loves you and is keeping the oath which he swore to your fathers, that the Lord has brought you out with a mighty hand, and redeemed you from the house of bondage, from the hand of Pharaoh king of Egypt. (7:6-8).

The tone and spirit of these passages express, better than any amount of comment upon them could, the sense of astonishment of Israel over the discovery of the uniqueness of her relationship to God, as well as the exclusively corporate character of this relationship. The idea which best expresses the nature and character of this relationship is that of *covenant.* Indeed, the covenant relationship between Israel and God is one of the central ideas and themes of the Bible. The nearest one can come to describing it in human terms is through analogy to the marriage bond. In comparing themselves with all the other peoples in the Fertile Crescent and the Arabian Desert with whom they had contact, and puzzling over the reasons for their own uniqueness which such comparison revealed, they could only conclude that God, in the deep mystery of his being, had selected them out of all these other peoples to be the special object of his love; much as a man selects a wife from among all the many women he knows. Just as the woman so selected would never thereafter really understand, but would simply and gratefully accept, the mystery of her selection, so Israel regarded and accepted the mystery of her special election and selection by Almighty God himself.

But marriage is not only selection; it also involves an exchange of vows, freely given and freely received, by which the two parties become committed to each other in an indissoluble personal bond. Something similar to this was recognized by Israel as being involved in her election by God as a necessary consequence of it. Only in this case, unlike the analogous situation in human marriage, the specific requirements placed upon Israel as her part of the covenant, the divine Law that is, had to be discovered slowly and haltingly as a part of the unfolding process of revelation in her history whereby her knowledge of God gradually increased and sharpened. Undoubtedly Moses was a key figure in this process of discovering the nature of God's requirements upon his chosen people. But the process had been going on before him and it certainly underwent extensive development after his time. Perhaps we have vestiges of the pre-Mosaic covenant codes in Exodus 34:14-26, and in the ceremony of the blessing and the curse at Shechem as recorded in Joshua 8:32-34 and in Deuteronomy 27:11-26. After Moses this process of developing understanding continued, as we can see from the stage which it had reached in the time of David and Solomon as reflected in the early source of Samuel.* Through the insights of the prophets from Amos to first Isaiah, the knowledge of God's demands upon his people increased greatly and soon after came to full flower in the Book of Deuteronomy near the end of the seventh century B.C.

The analogy of the covenant relationship between Israel and God to the human marriage bond was boldly developed by Hosea, when he compared Israel's apostasy, impurity, and self-centered seeking after her own ends to that of an adulterous wife. Just as no human hurt can compare with the anguish caused by adultery to one who deeply loves an unfaithful spouse, so nothing could compare with the anguish and terrible wrath of Almighty God which must follow upon the unrighteousness and unfaithfulness of the chosen people, with whom he has entered into a covenant. This same theme is developed in vivid, even glaring, detail later by Ezekiel (chapter 16). The author of Ephesians employs this same analogy between the new covenant and the marriage bond when he develops the thought of the Church as the bride of Christ, to "be presented before him in splendor, without spot or wrinkle or any such thing, that she might be holy and without blemish" (5:21-33).

It is this idea of a covenant between an entire people and God, experienced and acknowledged corporately in community and maintained continuously throughout a long history, which uniquely sets apart Israel and the Biblical revelation which came through her. Other instances of revelation through community exist, such as Hinduism, Chinese Taoism, or Japanese Shintoism, but instead of leading to a growing knowledge of the living God and the emergence of a sense of covenant relationship with him, they degenerated as time went on into a vast profusion of diverse deities and a confusion of uncoordinated numinous encounters. In other cases, such as Zoroaster, Mohammet, and the Guru Nanak, there have occurred isolated individual instances of divine encounters comparable to the greatest of the Hebrew Prophets.

* See, for example, *The Hebrew Iliad* by R. H. Pfeiffer and W. G. Pollard (New York: Harper, 1957).

These, however, although often leading subsequently to the formation of a community centered around the revelation received, were in their origin a radical break and an entirely new departure from the communities to which these individuals belonged. The great figures of Israel all contribute to, and further clarify, the great historic drama of revelation into which they were born and for which they thereafter represent landmarks along the way. The great religious figures elsewhere represent complete discontinuities with the cultures into which they were born, and the communities which were formed about the revelations which they gave have had ever after to stand or fall on the fullness and adequacy of the knowledge of God which they alone have revealed.

The uniqueness of Israel can be seen from a different vantage point in terms of the uniqueness of her literature, the Bible. No other people in all human history have ever dealt with their literature in such a way as to emerge with anything comparable to the Bible. In other cultures and civilizations the literary treasures of each generation have been preserved as distinct individual masterpieces, while other less distinctive writings have been forgotten and lost. With Israel, however, this preservation of the literary treasures of the past took place in a very different way. With her at each stage and turning point of her history all that had been written in the past was understood and used as a single whole, or corpus, whose sole function was to illumine her unique destiny and mission of knowing and revealing God. It is true that individual works, such as the J and E epics, Deuteronomy, and the several Prophets, continued to be known and to circulate independently for considerable periods after they were written. But there was simultaneously operative a strong drive to see all of this literature integrated into a single unitary expression of Israel's total accumulated understanding and witness so as to express as clearly and uniquely as possible her historic experience of God. In time the J and E epics were woven together so as to form one coherent version and the same was done with the early and late sources of Samuel. These in turn were connected with Deuteronomy and deuteronomic history so as to form a fairly coherent whole. A substantial body of other literature, such as court and temple annals, which was never incorporated into this central corpus, fell gradually into disuse and disappeared. In this way a continuous process of natural selection operated on the literature of Israel as an integral part of her history. Out of this process the Bible finally emerged, not by the arbitrary decision of any one individual or group, but gradually and naturally as the end product of a spontaneous and unplanned historic process. There is nothing comparable to this in all the rest of human history. No other people have emerged at cultural maturity with a single unitary collection of their total literature which grew with them throughout their history and emerged together with them as the natural embodiment of the essence and meaning of that history.

It is significant that much the same process took place with the literature of the Christian Church. This too was a completely unplanned natural process. Indeed it was not until late in the second century that the idea of specifically Christian holy scriptures began to emerge. Prior to then this literature was simply the "writings of the Apostles," which were revered by the several churches, but not thought of as scripture. Although by the time of Irenaeus the four Gospels and the Pauline corpus had acquired the status of a Holy Scripture nearly, if not then completely, on an equal footing with what we now call the Old Testament, it was not until much later that a comparable decision could be reached uniformly in all the churches with respect to the *Revelation of John*, or such books as *The Shepherd of Hermas*, the *Didache*, *Barnabas*, and *I Clement*. So it is that the New Testament emerged as the naturally evolved corporate expression and witness of the new Israel, the Catholic Church, in the same way and by the same unplanned process as the Old Testament emerged as the corporate expression and witness of the first Israel.

The recognition of this process of natural selection by which the Bible emerged seems to me vital to the firm establishment of its authenticity. For consider some of the consequences of this process. First, not one of the Biblical authors could possibly know whether anything he wrote would ultimately survive this proccss.

Regardless of the strength of their own convictions, or even of that of their contemporaries, about the truth and validity of the revelation they believed they had been given, every generation in Israel thereafter would apply to the writings left by each of them its own judgment based on all of the intervening history and experience of the whole people. Secondly, the selection of material at each stage was not governed by any preconceived plan or rational theory. As a result such radically conflicting views as Ecclesiastes and Second Isaiah, Deuteronomy and Job, Nahum and Jonah, or the first chapter of Genesis and its second and third chapters are all bound together in the same collection. Without regard to logic or consistency, everything which expressed a genuine element in Israel's total historic experience was retained, and everything else which ultimately did not contribute to her corporate understanding of her own peculiar destiny under God was rejected. Thirdly, this process means that literature coming from periods separated by as much as a thousand years and reflecting radically different cultural contexts and world views appears in it side by side. As a result the most primitive and the most advanced are placed side by side in the final collection, as one can see by comparing the song of Lamech in Genesis 4:23 ff. with the servant poem in Isaiah 53; or the Samson stories in Judges 13-16 with the Book of Ruth.

Seen in this way the Bible acquires a status which makes it an integral part of the actual historic process by which a whole people came to know God in community, by living out their complete history through every extreme of triumph and vicissitude, achievement and frustration, prosperity and adversity, within the revelatory intimacy of the bond of the covenant with him. It is not, as many have thought, that the Bible must be accorded a status and authority prior to and above the historic phenomenon that was Israel, so that one would make the Bible the authority for what happened in Israel. Rather the prime source for all that God has revealed of himself to man is the unique historic phenomenon that was Israel, and the Bible derives its authority from the circumstance that this same Israel produced it. God spoke to Israel through the covenant relationship, and Israel in turn has spoken to us through the Bible.. Some claims of contemporary Judaism to the contrary, Israel was not founded on the Old Testament, but rather the Old Testament was produced by Israel. In the same way—much contemporary Christianity to the contrary—the Church was not founded on the New Testament, but rather was the New Testament produced by the Church. There was, indeed, a flourishing and powerfully growing Church for at least twenty years before anything now in the New Testament began to be written.

If God has revealed himself to man, not through the reality of meeting and encounter in a covenant relationship with an historic people, but directly in words and sentences, phrases and propositions of his own framing, then the Bible is placed at a great disadvantage with respect to a book like the Koran, which makes precisely the same claim, but has the great advantage of having, at least in theory, been written by one man. The Koran is, indeed, much more suitable a vehicle for such a theory of revelation than is the Bible. It has a minimum of internal inconsistencies, is written in a single style from a single viewpoint, and avoids the embarrassment of having to place side by side both primitive and advanced material taken from radically different cultural contexts and epochs. If, as all Muslims and many Jews and Christians believe, God's revelation to man is contained in a book of divinely authenticated words and sentences, then do not the holy scriptures of Islam have a more reasonable claim to be this special book than do those of either Judaism or Christianity?

We may fruitfully pursue this same contrast along a somewhat different line by asking: why, if God's full revelation could be contained in a book of holy scripture, was it necessary for him also to enter into a covenant relationship with Israel, in view of all the terrible stresses and strains that relationship entailed over so many centuries? and especially, why it was necessary for the Son of God to come down from heaven for us men and for our salvation, for the Word to be made flesh and to dwell among us, and for Christ to suffer at the hands of wicked men, to die on the cross, and to rise again on the third day? Islam has none of this—no covenant and no Incarnation—but simply a man to whom God spoke, and who wrote his words in an orderly and coherent collection of Sûrahs so that all Muslims thereafter might have the benefit of God's whole revelation in a single volume of holy scriptures uncomplicated by any other auxiliary elements, such as acts or events in history. This thought suggests a paraphrase of Saint Paul that if salvation could come through a book (i.e., the Law), then Christ died for nothing (Gal. 2:21). Or again that if a book had been given which could make alive, then salvation would indeed be by such a book. "But the scripture consigned all things to sin, that what was promised to faith in Jesus Christ might be given to those who believe" (Gal. 3:22).

One small portion of the Bible which has received attention out of all proportion to its length as a result of theories of verbal and propositional revelation is the creation story in the first chapters of Genesis. It will help to illuminate the point which we are attempting to make here to examine in some detail the sources of this material in the Bible and the manner in which the Biblical authors dealt with it. The Hebrews were originally bedouin nomads of the Arabian Desert, and as such there is no evidence that they possessed any developed cosmology of their own. When they invaded Palestine from the desert and, after a long and indecisive period, were finally able under Saul and David to wrest the land from its native Canaanite inhabitants, they acquired in time from the civilized Canaanites among whom they settled the prevailing world view and primitive science which Canaan, in common with Syria and the rest of the settled peoples of the Fertile Crescent, had learned from the Babylonians. The civilization which flourished in Sumer and Akkad in the early centuries of the second millennium B.C. had made striking achievements in arithmetic, algebra, astronomy, and the development of a general systematic knowledge. This knowledge had spread to varying degrees among the other settled peoples who had contact with them. The bedouin Hebrews, with no corresponding systematic understandings of their own, would quite naturally in time absorb this native lore from the people they had conquered and among whom they settled. Such a process would require, as we know from many other similar instances, only a few generations to be essentially complete. Just as Oriental peoples today have acquired their science and technology from contact with the West, so Israel acquired her science from Babylonia through exposure to the Canaanites. There would certainly be no reason for them to disbelieve the new and illuminating insights which they gained in this way since they had nothing of their own to offer as a substitute, and since besides it represented the universally accepted view and belief of the civilized world which they entered from the desert and in which they settled.

Later on when the first written Hebrew literature appeared, it naturally reflected this prevailing understanding of the time whenever it needed to deal with scientific or cosmological material. Indeed it would have been completely ineffectual and even meaningless to those for whom it was written if it had been based on some completely new and previously unknown and foreign system of knowledge. Yet this is exactly what the proponents of the verbal revelation theory would have us believe. In their view the whole of the Pentateuch was delivered to Moses on Sinai in exactly the same way as the Koran is believed to have been delivered to Mohammet. Along with all the rest of the Pentateuch, the cosmology of the first chapters of Genesis was conveyed by the divine author as entirely new information, unrelated to any cultural context or prevailing system of belief. Such a view is not only shockingly incongruous with everything we now know about the structure and development of human culture, but it also seems to me to make a travesty of the very process of revelation itself, by removing it from any connection with the basic realities of human knowledge, experience, and history and by making it into an almost impersonal and highly artificial scheme for transmitting merely factual information.

Surely, however, if we treasure the necessity for seeing Israel as a real and authentic phenomenon in the actual history of the human race, we will demand that her literature, the Bible, be the living expression of a real people. Such a demand requires, however, that each component of it should, first of all, speak meaningfully and intelligibly to the particular cultural environment to which it was originally addressed and out of which it arose. Any literature, in any culture, which does not do this is not true literature. This demand implies, however, that the second and third chapters of Genesis must basically reflect the prevailing Babylonian cosmology of the ninth or tenth centuries B.C. during which they were written, and that the Priestly account in the first chapter must in turn reflect whatever development this world view had undergone in the whole Near Eastern world during the intervening five centuries which separate the Priest authors from Israel's first literature. Our expectations in this respect are reassuringly well confirmed by archeological evidence from this whole region as to what the prevailing world views in these two periods actually were. It would be a distortion of the whole idea of revelation as a real and valid means whereby the living God can become known to man through a covenant community, to attempt to find in Genesis 1 anything more than fifth-century B.C. Babylonian cosmology, or in Genesis 2 and 3 anything more than Babylonian science as it was understood in Palestine in the tenth century B.C. Contemporary efforts to reinterpret these accounts in a way which would imply that their authors had been given by some mysterious and magical insight a vision and understanding of twentieth-century A.D. cosmology, historical geology, and paleontology are not only misguided and fruitless, but actually harmful and misleading because they throw up an additional barrier which prevents us from perceiving the real function of the Bible; which is to communicate and witness to us in the twentieth century a vivid inside view of a people who, among all the peoples who have inhabited this earth, really came to know the living God in person, and who wrote the Bible, not to record systematic scientific knowledge in which they had no particular interest, but to share with each other and with us the burning reality of such knowledge and of man's necessary response to it.

All this is not to say, however, that the Biblical authors made no changes of any kind in the material of Babylonian origin which they used. Actually it was from a religious, rather than a scientific, standpoint that they changed it profoundly. The non-Biblical sources which have become available through excavations in Babylonia and elsewhere, such as the Ras Shamra tablets, exhibit a primitive polytheism and a picture of the nature and character of the gods of the most extreme crudity. In contrast to these sources the Biblical narratives of the same cosmological sequences manifest a lofty majesty and purity in the person of God, and in the character of his operation in events, which stands in the most striking contrast to the material with which they must have worked. Such comparisons are most impressive, and they reveal the truly remarkable power of Israel to touch, transform, and illuminate every area of human understanding in the light of the knowledge of the reality of the living God which had been revealed to her. Here one can see the process of revelation actually bearing fruit and operating on man's understanding of the world around him in the way in which God surely intended that his revelation of himself to man should work. In Job and II Isaiah we can already see the power of this vision of Almighty God at work on the prevailing Babylonian myths with their crude pictures of the role of the gods in the origin of the world and of man and their lack of a sense of contingency of all created things on One who transcends them. The process of illumination which they applied to the prevailing scientific knowledge of the world in their time in the light of their knowledge by revelation of the person of the living God, had come to full and general fruition in Israel by the time the Priest authors wrote the first chapter of Genesis. Our task today, if we would be true to the spirit and method of the Bible itself, is not to attempt to make fifth-century B.C. Babylonian cosmology conform with twentieth-century A.D. science, but rather to illuminate our scientific view of the world in the same way that the Biblical authors illuminated theirs. In *The Cosmic Drama,* a Faculty Paper, I have attempted to do something of this sort with one of the current cosmological theories. To me such an approach seems much more truly Biblical, and certainly to conform much more closely to the distinctive role of the Bible in revelation, than the more traditional approach of much of Christianity, which instead of contributing to understanding has only resulted in engaging the Church in a losing battle against the powerfully growing body of modern scientific knowledge.

The Role of the Spirit in Revelation

There is one aspect of the Biblical understanding of the nature and process of revelation which has not yet been touched upon, but which our discussion of the reality of spirit in Chapter III can assist us greatly in understanding. This is the role, so central to the whole New Testament, of the Holy Spirit in making available and accessible to all of the members of the Church the fullness of the knowledge of God which he has revealed in Christ through the Incarnation of the Word. Repeatedly in his last great address to them, Christ promised his disciples that when the Holy Spirit came to them he would teach them all things. "But when the Counselor comes, whom I shall send to you from the Father, even the Spirit of truth, who proceeds from the Father, he will bear witness to me" (St. John 15:26). "When the Spirit of truth comes, he will guide you into all the truth; for he will not speak on his own authority, but whatever he hears he will speak, and he will declare to you the things that are to come" (16:13). Afterwards it was, indeed, the experience of the Church that the knowledge which God had revealed was given to all in the holy community through the Holy Spirit, as one of several possible quotations from Saint Paul makes clear:

> 'What no eye has seen, nor ear heard'. . . . God has revealed to us through the Spirit. For the Spirit searches everything, even the depths of God. . . . No one comprehends the thoughts of God except the Spirit of God. Now we have received not the spirit of the world but the Spirit which is from God, that we might understand the gifts bestowed on us by God. And we impart this in words not taught by human wisdom but taught by the Spirit, interpreting spiritual truths to those who possess the Spirit. (I Cor. 2:9-13)

This teaching function of the spirit is indeed a universal characteristic and function of the spirit in all communities, including the science community. The spirit in a community is the dynamo, or source of power, by means of which the community expresses itself and its members gain insight and understanding of the deepest things in the life of the community. The spirit, therefore, is the source of that which we call "inspiration." Every human community or culture which has expressed itself in a literature has done so through the power which it had to inspire a chosen few of its members to set into words insights and understandings peculiar to, and emerging out of, its life. But if we inquire into the source and dynamism of such inspiration, we shall certainly find the answer to our question in the spirit which activates the community. Neither inspiration nor spirit are specifically religious categories, for they apply with equal force to all communities including pagan or completely secular ones—even, indeed, to such a militantly anti-religious community as Russian Communism. The uniqueness of the inspiration of the Biblical authors is not to be found in any special kind of process or spiritual phenomenon not encountered in other cultures, for it is identical to the process by which Greek or Roman or Chinese authors were inspired. Rather it is to be found in the uniqueness of the community of Israel and of the spirit which empowered that community and was the source of such inspiration. Because of her unique function as a people, which was to meet and to know God and to live out her history in a covenant relationship with him, Israel always believed that the spirit which dwelt in her, unlike those with other peoples, was none other than the Spirit of God himself. However, just as the climax and fulfillment of the drama of revelation which Israel enacted in her history came in the Incarnation of the Son of God in Christ, whereby the knowledge of God which it was Israel's special destiny to reveal was made concrete, so in the same way the fact that the spirit which dwelt in the community of Israel was none other than the Spirit of God himself was made concrete and clearly and directly evident in the gift of the Holy Spirit to Christ's Church at Pentecost.

Christ as the Ultimate Revelation

The event of Pentecost represents the formation of a new holy community out of the old Israel. In this event a new testament and a new covenant were actualized in the life of a new Israel, the Church. Between this event and the old Israel stands a single individual, Jesus Christ, the Son of God. In order to complete our discussion of the problem of revelation, it is necessary to consider the place of Christ in the process by which revelation takes place.

If, as we have argued, the distinctive feature of revelation in its Biblical sense is its communal character involving the total history of a people, as opposed to revelation through individual religious leaders as in other religions, then it might appear that the revelation of God in Christ contradicts this principle. It is sometimes supposed, for example, that Christ stands in the same relationship to Christians as does Mohammet to Muslims, Gautama Buddha to Buddhists, or Zoroaster to Zoroastrians. Considered in this way the revelation of God through Jesus of Nazareth seems to constitute a discontinuity with Judaism in which a totally new religion came to be founded on the teachings of a single individual. If such an interpretation were to be accepted, then all that we have said so far about the Biblical understanding of revelation as a continuous process in the life and experience of a community would not apply to the Christian revelation.

The problem raised by such considerations is, however, based on a complete misunderstanding of the place and role of Christ both with respect to Israel before him and the Church after him. We can see this both in looking forward toward Christ from the vantage point of the old Israel into which he came as the culmination and climax of the drama which constitutes her long history, as well as by looking backward to Christ from the vantage point of the new Israel, his Church, in the light of the Apostolic witness. When we do so, we shall see that the revelation of God in Christ, far from constituting an apparent exception to the distinctive

Biblical doctrine of revelation as we have described it, is really the ultimate and complete fulfillment of that doctrine.

First, when we consider the place of Christ from the vantage point of Israel, we see that he came not as a new departure or a break with the old, but rather as the fulfillment of expectations long expressed and as the completion of that which God had been revealing of himself through all the triumphs and vicissitudes of Israel's long history. The old covenant was recognized throughout by those who were involved in it as incomplete. All the prophets bear testimony to their sense of involvement in a drama which was still unfolding and leading toward some great future climax and completion. The statement, "Behold, the days are coming, says the Lord, when I will make a new covenant with the house of Israel" (Jer. 31:31), is characteristic of such expectations. Most particularly the literature of the late post-exilic period preceding the coming of Christ (Daniel, Zechariah 9-14, Enoch, etc.) is filled with a strange tenseness of expectation and charged with the conviction that God was preparing to act in some decisive way. When finally, in the words of the creed, "the Son of God, for us men and for our salvation, came down from heaven, and was incarnate by the Holy Ghost and the Virgin Mary, and was made man," this event was simply the expected completion and fulfillment of the long drama of revelation and response which had been unfolding on the stage of history ever since the call of Abraham. The way in which the coming of Christ was seen within Israel as the completion of the old covenant is nowhere more forcefully expressed than in the song of Zacharias:

Blessed be the Lord God of Israel; for he hath visited and redeemed his people;
And hath raised up a mighty salvation for us, in the house of his servant David;
As he spake by the mouth of his holy Prophets, which have been since the world began;
That we should be saved from our enemies, and from the hand of all that hate us.
To perform the mercy promised to our forefathers, and to remember his holy covenant;

To perform the oath which he sware to our forefather Abraham, that he would give us;
That we being delivered out of the hand of our enemies, might serve him without fear;
In holiness and righteousness before him, all the days of our life. (St. Luke 1:68-75)

The revelation of God in Christ is, therefore, seen to be integral with, and the fulfillment of, his revelation through Israel. As Jesus himself expressed it, "Think not that I have come to abolish the law and the prophets; I have come not to abolish them but to fulfil them" (St. Matthew 5:17). Revelation remains a communal, as opposed to an individual, process. It is only that the revelation given in and through community remains partially hidden and incomplete until it can be gathered up and focused in a single person. But the Incarnation by itself would have been meaningless and unrecognizable if it had not come as the climax of a drama in community. From time to time throughout its history the true community of Israel was greatly reduced in numbers and represented by only a small remnant of the faithful. In the end at the climax of the drama, this remnant was finally reduced to a single individual who represented from the standpoint of humanity the very essence of Israel, the fulfillment of all that the community had been leading up to; and from the standpoint of divinity, him in whom "all the fullness of God was pleased to dwell" and through whom God would "reconcile to himself all things, whether on earth or in heaven, making peace by the blood of his cross" (Colossians 1:19,20).

If now, in place of looking at Christ in anticipation from the vantage point of Israel, we view him in retrospect from the vantage point of the Church, we see equally clearly his integral continuity with Israel and the revelation which came through Israel. The New Testament is rooted and grounded in the Old. There is no discontinuity between them, but rather the one is the completion and fulfillment of the other. Through the Church all that had been so obscure and hidden in Israel of the purposes and character of God had now been made known in Christ, even "to the principalities and powers in the heavenly places," as the Epistle to the Ephesians says, so that all men could now "see what is the plan of the mystery hidden for ages in God who created all things" (3:9,10). "For he has made known to us in all wisdom and insight the mystery of his will, according to his purpose which he set forth in Christ, as a plan for the fullness of time, to unite all things in heaven and things on earth" (1:9,10). Such a passage powerfully sets forth the distinctive New Testament proclamation of Christ as the ultimate revelation of God in and through Israel, and of his place and role as an integral part of thc long drama in history of which he was the climax and completion.

The Church, like Israel, is a holy community living in a covenant relationship with God. But these two communities are in no sense discontinuous or unrelated to each other. They are bridged, to be sure, by a single person, but this person stands uniquely for both communities. He did not stand in isolation from them, but rather gathered together and summed up in his own person all that the old was destined to be and all that the new could potentially become. Biblically speaking, Israel and the Church are one single community in full historic continuity. At one point in the history of this community, it was narrowed down to a remnant consisting of only a single person. From that point on, through the life, death, and resurrection of this Person, the community reformed itself again at Pentecost, fulfilled and completed, and thereafter grew powerfully and irresistibly, breaking out of the narrow confines of Judaism and spreading over the whole world. This turning point does not, therefore, constitute an exception in which the individual is contrasted over against the communal, but rather a narrowing of the communal into the personal. Before his coming, he was anticipated as the fulfillment toward which the whole historic existence of the community had been leading. After he had come, the community could best express its own peculiar nature and special quality by knowing itself to be a holy and mystical body which was none other than the very Body of Christ himself.

The person who stands between the old Israel and the new, between the old covenant and the new, does not do so as a religious leader founding a new religion. He is not, like Mohammet or Zoroaster, a man to whom God spoke in some new and unprecedented way so as to inaugurate a new religion. The supposition by Marcion that he was, together with the corollary rejection of Israel and the Old Testament, was quickly branded as heresy in the early Church. Jesus left no writings, his ministry was phenomenally brief and tragically terminated, and he left behind him no developed plan nor organization to carry it out. Neither in his own eyes nor in those of the Church was he thought of as a prophet or teacher to whom God had revealed himself and through whom knowledge of God was transmitted to men. Rather he was himself God incarnate, so that to know him was to know the Father. It is not primarily through his teachings and deeds that he revealed God, but rather in his own person, in his life, death, and resurrection, that God has made himself known to men so that they "have beheld his glory; glory as of the only Son from the Father." God was revealed *in* him, rather than *through* him. This distinction sums up the whole Biblical understanding of revelation by divine act and deed through a holy community, and resolves as well the apparent problem posed at the outset of this section in which Christianity was made to appear to be a new religion founded by a single religious leader who claimed a revelation from God.

Summary

We shall attempt in conclusion to summarize the point of view with respect to the nature of revelation in its Biblical sense which we have been developing here. In the first place Israel, in common with most other cultures, early in her history had frequent corporate numinous experiences of the mystery of the divine presence, who at that stage can only be designated as the *mysterium tremendum*. In this first stage Israel was not unique but simply shared, in perhaps a rather more vivid and intense way, experiences common to many peoples in the presence of storm or volcano, sea or mountain, or other occasion for the numinous. Secondly, however, this experience elicited from Israel a truly unique response by way of actually meeting the Being thus mysteriously experienced, and entering into a permanent relationship with him which was to last throughout her whole subsequent history as a people and become the central theme and primary focus of its whole historic existence. This relationship was eventually apprehended in terms of the idea of the "covenant." Through it every turning point in Israel's history and every major event in her corporate existence as a people became illuminated by her intimate knowledge of the living God, so that the presence of God in these events "with a mighty hand, and an outstretched arm," acting both to save and to judge, was perceived and made known. Through the preservation of this covenant relationship and through the revelatory power of these events throughout the whole unfolding drama of her existence in history, God became known to Israel as he has to no other people. Finally, at the great climax of this drama on the stage of human history, God himself entered upon a human life within this community of Israel, becoming incarnate in Jesus Christ, so that all that can be known of God in the finite human estate might be made manifest through him. The opening verses of the Epistle to the Hebrews powerfully summarize this whole drama of revelation:

> In many and various ways God spoke of old to our fathers by the prophets; but in these last days he has spoken to us by a Son, whom he appointed the heir of all things, through whom also he created the world. He reflects the glory of God and bears the very stamp of his nature, upholding the universe by his word of power." (1:1-3)

The revelation of God has come to man in act and deed, in confrontation and meeting, within the life and experience of a chosen people, culminating in Christ through the supreme revelatory act of the Incarnation, the Word made flesh and dwelling among us. The community which experienced this revelation and lived within the grip of its power has expressed itself to us through a literature, the Bible, which grew with the community and emerged in history with it as its single corporate witness for all mankind to the revelation which it alone had experienced. Because of the uniqueness of its relationship with the living God, the spirit which empowered this community, first dimly as the old Israel and later with the full power of Pentecost as the Church, was none other than the Holy Spirit, the Spirit of God himself. By this Spirit the Prophets and the Apostles were inspired to express in words the deep meanings and insights into the nature and person of Almighty God and his ways with his creation, which this community alone possessed. These words are Holy Scripture, the Word of God for the salvation of man, not because of any special quality which they possess in themselves as words, but because the spirit dwelling in the community which wrote them is God the Holy Spirit. Holy Scripture bears the same relationship to God the Holy Spirit as the literature of any other people or community bears to the spirit of that community. The authority of the Bible rests not in itself but in Israel and Christ out of which it bears witness, and in the Holy Spirit under whose power it was written.

The question of the authority of the Bible raises the problem of the validity of revealed knowledge. Until my full incorporation into the Church several years ago I had assumed, as I suppose most scientists and many others do, that the question had already been essentially settled and that the only kind of knowledge capable of validation was scientific knowledge. It seemed obvious that any kind of knowledge, so called, which had been gained through revelation was incapable of validation but, if accepted at all, could only be taken blindly on faith. Since coming to share to the full the life of the community of the faithful in Christ Jesus in the Church, however, my views on this question have changed radically. I now see no fundamental or essential difference in the basis on which I hold the knowledge I have as a member of the community of physics to be valid and true knowledge, and that on which I hold the knowledge I have as a member of the Catholic Church to be valid and true knowledge. This point I have perhaps already made sufficiently clear in the first chapter. Here I need only point out again that the validation of all forms of knowledge is necessarily the exclusive function of the community which possesses the knowledge. It is not possible for anyone but a physicist to really know the truth of physics; everyone else has to take it on faith. Equally so it is not possible for anyone but a fully involved and committed Christian to really know the truth of Christianity. Purely by way of personal witness out of my own experience in both communities, I can simply assert that the knowledge I believe I have of the truth of Christianity and my sense of conviction as to its essential validity and reality rests on just as good and just as firm and convincing grounds as the knowledge I believe I have of the truth of physics and my sense of conviction as to the essential validity of the view of reality which the community of physics has presently achieved. Having said this, however, I am aware that I would have just as difficult a time convincing an oriental mystic who profoundly disbelieved in the reality of physics that the statement makes sense, as I now have in convincing a scientific colleague who profoundly disbelieves in the reality of the Gospel. This simply means that all knowledge comes through community and that it is only within the community in which it is known that the question of its validity can ultimately be settled. On this basis the validity of that which has become known of God through his self-revelation in Christ has been thoroughly, and indeed most adequately, tested through two thousand years of the life of a great historic community within which this knowledge has been received and transmitted, and out of which witness to it has been borne in every generation.

Author's Note

BOOKS, pamphlets, and articles cited in the text:

Brown, Harcourt, ed. *Science and the Creative Spirit.* Toronto: University of Toronto Press, 1958.

Buber, Martin. *I and Thou.* New York: Scribner's, 1958.

Chambers, Whittaker. *The Witness.* New York: Random House, 1952.

Compton, Arthur. *Atomic Quest.* New York: Oxford University Press, 1956.

Crossman, Richard. *The God That Failed.* New York: Harper & Bros., 1950.

Heim, Karl. *Christian Faith and Natural Science.* New York: Harper & Bros., 1953.

Heisenberg, Werner. *Philosophical Problems of Nuclear Science.* New York: Pantheon, 1952.

———. "A Scientist's Case for the Classics," *Harper's Magazine,* May 1958, p. 29.

Hoffer, Eric. *The True Believer.* New York: Harper & Bros., 1951.

Homans, George. *The Human Group.* New York: Harcourt Brace, 1950.

Mead, Margaret, and Metraux, Rhoda. "Image of the Scientist among High School Students" in *Science,* 126 (August 30, 1957): p. 384.

Miller, Arthur. *The Crucible.* New York: Viking, 1953.

Oldham, J. H. *Life Is Commitment.* New York: Harper & Bros., 1952.

Otto, Rudolf. *The Idea of the Holy.* 2nd Edition. New York: Oxford University Press, 1950.

Oppenheimer, J. Robert. *Science and the Common Understanding.* New York: Simon and Schuster, 1954.

Paton, Alan. "The Person in Community," a chapter in *The Christian Idea of Education,* edited by Edmund Fuller. New Haven: Yale University Press, 1957.

Pfeiffer, R. H. and Pollard, W. G. *The Hebrew Iliad.* New York: Harper & Bros., 1957.

Polanyi, Michael. *Personal Knowledge:* Towards a Post-critical Philosophy. Chicago: University of Chicago Press, 1958.

Pollard, William G. *Chance and Providence.* New York: Scribner's, 1958.

———. *The Cosmic Drama.* New York: National Council, Protestant Episcopal Church, 1954. A pamphlet in the "Faculty Papers" series.

Redfield, Robert. *The Little Community.* Chicago: University of Chicago Press, 1955.

Schilling, Harold. "On Relating Science and Religion," in *The Christian Scholar,* 41 (September 1958): p. 376.

———. "A Human Enterprise" in *Science,* 127 (June 1958): p. 1324.

Snow, C. P. *The Search.* New York: Scribner's, 1958.

Temple, William. *Nature, Man, and God.* London: Macmillan, 1949.